## "I ... You Tonight, Duarte."

He looked at Linda with an expression that chilled her. "What, might I ask, is the reason for this sudden aversion you have for me?"

Linda shook her head. "It's not an aversion."

"No?" His straight dark eyebrow lifted. "Perhaps you will explain it to me then?"

"I can't explain," she whispered, hanging her head.

Duarte gripped her wrist and brought her to him, crushing her lips with his own. "You made a bargain with me," he said at last. "Don't think I will allow you to change your mind."

---

**ANNE HAMPSON**

currently makes her home in England, but this top romance author has traveled and lived all over the world. This variety of experience is reflected in her books, which present the ever-changing face of romance as it is found wherever people fall in love.

Dear Reader:

Silhouette has always tried to give you exactly what you want. When you asked for increased realism, deeper characterization and greater length, we brought you Silhouette Special Editions. When you asked for increased sensuality, we brought you Silhouette Desire. Now you ask for books with the length and depth of Special Editions, the sensuality of Desire, but with something else besides, something that no one else offers. Now we bring you SILHOUETTE INTIMATE MOMENTS, true romance novels, longer than the usual, with all the depth that length requires. More sensuous than the usual, with characters whose maturity matches that sensuality. Books with the ingredient no one else has tapped: excitement.

There is an electricity between two people in love that makes everything they do magic, larger than life—and this is what we bring you in SILHOUETTE INTIMATE MOMENTS. Look for them wherever you buy books.

These books are for the woman who wants more than she has ever had before. These books are for you. As always, we look forward to your comments and suggestions. You can write to me at the address below:

Karen Solem
Editor-in-Chief
Silhouette Books
P.O. Box 769
New York, N.Y. 10019

# ANNE HAMPSON
# Sweet Second Love

*Silhouette Romance*

Published by Silhouette Books New York

**America's Publisher of Contemporary Romance**

SILHOUETTE BOOKS, a Simon & Schuster Division of
GULF & WESTERN CORPORATION
1230 Avenue of the Americas, New York, N.Y. 10020

ISBN: 0-671-57226-1

First Silhouette Books printing June, 1983

10 9 8 7 6 5 4 3 2 1

Map by Ray Lundgren

America's Publisher of Contemporary Romance

Printed in the U.S.A.

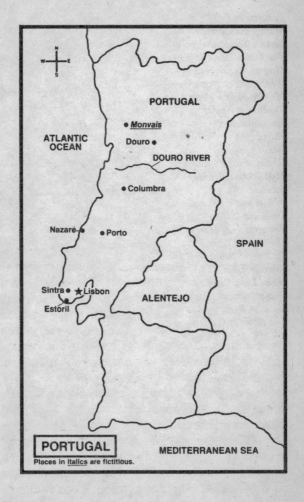

PORTUGAL

Places in _italics_ are fictitious.

# Chapter One

Linda Kendall's forehead was creased in a frown as she pondered on the offer made to her earlier that day, relayed to her by her aunt. She could have a free holiday in Portugal if she agreed to accompany three children on the flight, children who were to join their uncle at his home at Monvais, in the Douro Valley. She would get her first class return fare, an unbelievably large amount of money as 'wages,' and a week at an hotel.

'You ought to accept,' advised her aunt with whom Linda had lived since the accident which had killed her husband and their two children—twins only three years old. Although it had happened almost two years ago Linda was no nearer to recovery from the shock than she had been at the time. Night and day the horror of it was with her;

she had lost weight, could neither eat nor sleep, had no interest in her appearance so that now, still only twenty-six years old, she looked as if there were at least another ten years on her age.

'You think that a week—or perhaps a day or so longer—will cure this pain?' Linda felt ungrateful, because Auntie Sal had been so wonderful, insisting on having her come to live with her even though the old lady had often admitted she liked being on her own. She was like that, one of those exceedingly self-sufficient people who needed little more in life than books to make her last years of life pleasant and complete. That she had disrupted the set and smooth way of life of her aunt Linda very well knew, and she would have stayed in her own home but Auntie Sal had turned up one day and declared she would not leave without her.

So understanding! The old lady had in fact suffered a loss herself some twenty years ago when she lost her only son in a climbing accident. A widow already, she was left almost alone in the world and so she had a sort of kindred feeling and insight into just how her niece was feeling.

'It won't cure the pain, love,' she answered in that gruff but compassionate voice which now was so familiar to Linda. 'But it'll make a break. For over two years you haven't done anything but sit around, letting your grief take over completely. You ought to get a job, dear, just so you could be out, meeting people. However, that's for later: for now, well, this little task and trip seem heaven-sent to me and I feel you'd not only be doing yourself a disservice if you refused, but Alice would feel slighted because, after all, she picked on you especially owing to the way you are.'

Linda nodded absently. It was true that for two years she had stayed indoors, crying and thinking . . . dwelling all the time on her loss. It was no use telling herself—as Auntie sometimes told her— that others had suffered similar tragedies and had managed eventually to recover. Linda felt she did not want to recover and that, said her aunt, was the main trouble. Linda had had a wonderful husband and two lovely children whom she adored. A happier family could never have been found.

And in one stroke all was gone.

Linda always bemoaned the fact that when David had suggested she come as well, when he went to see his mother on that fateful Saturday morning, she had said she really must do some overdue chores as her friend and her husband were to come on a visit the following Tuesday. David was only going to take some cakes and pies which Linda had baked for his mother. It was to be a quick visit since David had things to do to the car, its being week-end and his having time off.

'If only I'd gone as well,' she had wept. 'I'd have died too.'

Her aunt had wept then, but maintained quite firmly that one day Linda would learn to live again.

'If you mean that I'll meet someone else—' She shook her head emphatically. 'No other man shall ever take David's place.'

'No, my love,' was her aunt's soothing agreement. 'But maybe a lovely man will find his own place in your heart.'

No more was said as Linda made it plain that she could not bear such talk.

'Do promise you'll give the trip some thought,' begged Auntie Sal, cutting into her niece's thought stream. 'As I mentioned, Alice Sutherland was the children's nanny but had to retire through ill-health.' She stopped abruptly, her eyes registering impatience. 'You know all this,' she added frowning. 'The main thing is that these children must go to their uncle to be looked after until their mother is out of hospital, and that could be a long time—probably a few months—from now. Their father went off with someone else. . . .' Her voice faded. Linda knew this also. The children's mother was Portuguese, their father English. It was the mother's brother who was offering to take them under his care, because there was no one else and their mother had been greatly troubled at the possibility of their having to be taken into care.

'Yes,' answered Linda, when her aunt repeated her question. 'I'll give the trip some thought.'

She went to see Alice Sutherland the following morning. The sun shone down from a cloudless blue sky and all the glory of spring was before her eyes as she sat on the bus which traversed lovely winding lanes, the budding trees meeting overhead in many cases. England in spring!

How she and David had loved their garden in the spring when the bushes they had planted together had begun to bud and then flower, when the daffodils flared golden against the soft green lawn they had made from what had been a stony wilderness of weeds and trailing brambles.

Tears. . . . She dried them and wished she could die. No use dear auntie being so emphatic about the eventual recovery. It would be disloyal to David and the children if she did recover, she always told herself.

Alice was middle-aged and had had a stroke but she was managing now to do things for herself. She had been shattered when the marriage of her beloved mistress had broken up, and even more shattered when she had had to leave her because of her health. Marianna Skipton had been a wonderful employer. Born into the Portuguese aristocracy, she had in effect had a marriage arranged for her with a nobleman—friend of her brother—but she had rebelled and gone off with Frederick Skipton, the Englishman she had met while she was visiting friends in London. It had been a whirlwind courtship, and for a time the marriage had been happy. Alice had been brought in when the first child, Vasco, was on the way, and she had stayed on, living as one of the family, until she had the stroke six months ago. Marianna had then managed without help, but a week ago she had taken ill and on admittance to hospital she was found to have a serious disease which would take at least three months to cure. Alice had taken the children but already they were too much for her.

'I'd love to keep them until dear Marianna comes out of hospital,' she told Linda as she sat in the woman's small parlour drinking coffee. 'But even if I could their uncle would not agree. He's a very determined man—dictatorial, I would say. Mari-anna phoned him and he immediately told her that the children must go to him. She was relieved of course and so was I because it'd break my heart to see those little ones go into the care of a soulless authority. Besides, should anything happen to their mother, they'll now at least be taken care of until they grow up.'

Linda frowned at the idea of their mother's dying but all she said was,

'This uncle—you've met him?'

'Several times. You see, I always accompanied the family when they went on holiday to visit the Conde—'

'Conde?' broke in Linda, interested. 'He's ti-tled?'

'Oh, yes, indeed. The Conde Duarte Alfonso Laurenco de Dominga is one of the highest in the land. So it was sad that his sister married so far beneath her. However, to get back to the Conde—we call him Dom Duarte, Dom being equal to "lord" in this country. If you address him then do remember to say "Dom Duarte" won't you?'

'I haven't said I'll take the children, Mrs. Suther-land.'

'But you must, dear. It'll be good for them to have someone like you, and also for you—well, your aunt's troubled about you, dear, and so you'll be making her happy if you take this little break.'

'I don't like the idea of being on my own in an hotel in a strange country,' murmured Linda know-ing full well she would brood and weep and proba-bly stay in her room all the time.

12

'Well, now. . . .' The woman paused as if she were carefully choosing her words. 'I've been in touch with Dom Duarte on the phone and he feels that whoever brings the children should stay with them for a few days. Oh, they know him well enough,' submitted Alice on noting Linda's start of surprise. 'Yes, they are used to him all right because they visit twice a year at least—or did do until their daddy went off. But Dom Duarte's thinking that the children will need someone until he can get a nanny for them.'

Linda was nodding in agreement now. She couldn't imagine the children just being dumped and left, even though they did know their uncle. How *well* did they know him? A twice yearly visit wasn't much, since to a child six months' interval could be a very long time. Undoubtedly the children would not know their uncle intimately.

She sipped her coffee, declined the biscuits offered and said, her big grey eyes darkened, as always, with sadness,

'Auntie Sal did tell me a bit about the children, but I'd like to know more. Vasco's the oldest—he's eight?'

'That's right. Then comes Felix who's seven and Clara who will be six in November—well, that actually makes her five and a half now.'

'So they'd not be too much trouble to take. . . .' Linda let her voice trail to silence, rather amazed that she should seriously be considering the offer made by the children's uncle. As she had just remarked, she wouldn't like to be alone in an hotel; but if she were to be kept on at the Palacio

Dominga for a few days then she need not take the week's holiday offered. She could come straight home.

'Will you do it, dear?' from Alice on an anxious note. 'Dom Duarte asked me to find someone and so did Marianna. If you refuse I really don't know who to ask. I'd not care to advertise, for I don't know what kind of a person I'd get.' She paused, then added persuasively, 'Even leaving yourself out of it you'd be helping their mother and uncle, the children themselves, your aunt and me.'

At that a rare smile, the ghost of a smile, touched the wide and generous line of Linda's mouth.

'You're holding a gun at my head, Mrs. Sutherland,' she accused.

'I do hope you'll do this,' was all Alice said. But she looked hopeful, optimistic, noticed Linda, and it was then that her mind was made up. But she wanted to see the children who, her aunt had said, were lively. At present they were at the local school, Alice having managed to persuade the headmistress to accept them as she could not have them for the whole of the day. The headmistress was an understanding woman and so Alice did have the rest she needed during the daytime.

'Yes, you can see them this afternoon,' she agreed in response to Linda's request. 'Shall you come back—or you could have lunch here and wait—'

'No, it isn't too far for me to go home and come back at about six this evening. Will that time be all right for you?' Linda caught sight of herself in a

14

mirror on the wall and for the very first time since
the tragedy she felt slightly ashamed of her appearance. Her hair hadn't been washed for over two
weeks and it was straggly and greasy; her face was
sunken and sallow, her clothes were shabby. She
closed her eyes for a moment, remembering with
poignant intensity the way David had always admired her beauty. She would keep it till she was
old, he had declared, for it was the kind of beauty
that never fades. How little he had known when
those words were uttered!

'Yes,' Alice was saying eagerly in answer to
Linda's query, 'this evening around six will be fine.'

When Linda arrived back at her aunt's house the
old lady was in the garden, pushing the mower.

'Give me that,' said Linda at once. 'Why aren't
you leaving the lawn for Donald to do?' Donald
was a 'jobber' who came in once a fortnight.

'His wife's just rung in to say he's in bed with a
bad back.' Auntie Sal's lined, good-natured face
pulled in a grimace. 'If you ask me it's lazyitis that
gardener's suffering from! In bed! And he's only
forty years of age! I'd rub his back with a brick if I
was his wife.'

Linda said that perhaps this was a harsh conclusion and that Donald really did have something the
matter with his back.

'It's the sort of complaint no one ever receives
sympathy for,' she ended as she took hold of the
handles of the mower. 'I saw Mrs. Sutherland,' she
added when she saw the questioning look in her
aunt's pale blue eyes. 'I'm going to see the children
this evening. Are you coming with me?'

'I might.'

'I think I shall accept the offer.' She began pushing the mower slowly across the lawn. Her aunt walked beside her.

'I'm glad, dear. As I said, those children are lively so you'll earn your money. Take some games and books to keep them occupied on the airplane or you might have trouble. One thing: it's not a long flight.'

'Not too long,' agreed Linda. She was at the end of the lawn and she swung the mower around to face the other way. 'The uncle,' she said reflectively, 'he sounds rather overpowering.'

'How do you mean? What did Alice say about him?'

'Oh, not a lot. It's his name.'

'That!' Auntie Sal gave a laugh. 'Conde something-and-something-and something de Dominga. Is that right?'

For the first time in two years Linda laughed. Her aunt stared but wisely made no comment. She was feeling rather pleased with herself for putting her niece's name forward immediately on Alice Sutherland's mentioning the children and the need for someone to take them safely over to Portugal and the uncle who had offered to take them into his care.

'If I remember rightly it's The Conde Duarte Alfonso Laurenco de Dominga, but I have to address him as Dom Duarte.'

'I should hope so! How could anyone be expected to get one's tongue round a name like that.'

'His home is called the Palacio Dominga. It's a palace, obviously.'

'Well, he *is* the nobility so his home is bound to be something special.'

'It must be very grand.' A hint of awe crept into Linda's voice.

'I expect so. Alice used to say it was gracious and dignified, that the whole aspect was one of wealth and good taste, that there was a sort of serenity about the grounds, which extended over many acres, and there are terraces and parterres and fountains and lily ponds. However, I don't suppose you will be seeing much of it, more's the pity. You'll be coming away from the Palacio as soon as you've delivered the children, I guess.' They were at the other end of the lawn and as Linda swung the mower around again her aunt told her to leave the rest until tomorrow.

'Mrs. Sutherland was saying that the Conde suggested I stay a few days, just until the children became used to being there.'

'He did?' Although the old lady's face brightened at this she did say, 'But the children *are* used to being there?'

'Not really. In any case, the Conde wants me to stay until he gets a nanny for them. I expect it will be a week at the very most but probably less.'

'Then you'll have your week's holiday in the hotel. That'll be a very nice long break for you, dear.'

'I shan't stay in the hotel, Auntie. I'll come home when I leave the Palacio.'

'But—'

'I don't want to be on my own, Auntie.'

'No, love, I understand.'

Auntie Sal did decide to accompany Linda that evening when she went to meet the three children. It was still fine and warm and not even dusk by the time they arrived at ten minutes to six. The children were in the small garden, playing with a large beach ball.

'Let's have a cup of tea first,' suggested Alice who already had the kettle on the boil. 'I've told them you're coming, Linda—you don't mind if I call you Linda, do you, dear?'

'No, of course not.' Her eyes strayed to the window, which was open a few inches at the top, allowing voices to drift into the room.

'Vasco—you're kicking it too hard!'

'Well, you're a girl and can't run fast enough to get it!'

'Felix, make him kick it gentler!'

Auntie Sal smiled and said,

'They've all been given Portuguese names, it seems. The girl, you said, is Clara?'

'That's right. However, I remember there was a compromise after Vasco. Felix can be English and so can Clara. Marianna wanted names like José and Felipe and Casimira and Rosalia.'

'Will Marianna eventually return to Portugal?' asked Auntie Sal conversationally and Alice nodded her head at once.

'I think that she stayed on here because she

hoped her husband would return to her and the children, but time has passed and as it's now unlikely, she did mention that she would like to return to her own country.'

'It's only natural,' from Auntie Sal. 'Poor thing. And her so highly born.'

'Yes; they're a very exalted family. The Conde is an arrogant man, full of his own importance and always conscious of the nobility from which he stems and to which he belongs. The Dominga estates are vast; they grow cork and citrus fruits; they have vineyards and they grow lots of other things besides. Dom Duarte is also in commerce. Apart from the vineyards he is in the wine retailing business too. He's a very wealthy man—a millionaire several times over.' Alice fell silent, thinking. She had poured the tea and she gestured for Linda and her aunt to help themselves to sugar. 'Dom Duarte is thirty later this year and will shortly marry, I shouldn't wonder.'

'He's engaged?' Auntie Sal looked interested.

'Not unless it's happened recently, for Marianna hasn't ever mentioned it. But he has a very lovely girl friend whom everyone expects him to marry. She's Dona Lucia Mendes, daughter of Dom Ronaldo de Mendes, another of the nobility of the region. It will be an excellent match, Marianna says.'

Linda merely sat and listened to this interchange between the two older women.

'Is this woman titled? I mean,' said Auntie Sal, 'is Dona a title in Portugal?'

'No, every woman is a Dona. The wife of a Dom would be a Dona. Dom, by the way, is a hereditary title. Not every Portuguese man is a Dom.'

'Sounds a bit complicated.'

'It isn't. One gets used to it—well, I have because I've been over there so many times.'

'Well, Linda will be getting used to it this time next week, I reckon.' Auntie Sal regarded her niece affectionately, thinking how pretty she used to be when happiness gave a glow to her lovely eyes, and health a bloom to her cheeks. She had a perfect skin, but these days it had acquired a sallow tint which unfortunately added ten years to her age. The Conde would take her for at least thirty-five, decided Auntie Sal, feeling depressed, which wasn't like her at all for she was always described as 'a happy soul.'

'I think you'd better bring the children in,' suggested Linda glancing at her watch. 'Auntie and I don't very much like going home after dark these days.'

'No; I can understand. I hate living alone but what can one do? It's awful when you have to be afraid like this. My only consolation is that those thugs who attack old people will be attacked themselves one day, when they get old.'

Linda frowned.

'What an awful thought.'

'Afraid I'm the vindictive kind,' admitted Alice. 'I believe in an eye for an eye and a tooth for a tooth, and I always shall.' Rising from the chair, she went to the door and called to the children, who all came in immediately. It was easy to see that for all her apparent softness Alice had been a keen disciplinarian in her role of nanny to Marianna's children.

'This is Linda—Mrs. Kendall. She's the lady who'll be going on the airplane with you to your uncle's.' All three stood very still and looked hard at Linda, faces serious.

'Hello, Mrs. Kendall.' Vasco was the first to speak. He had looked Linda over, from her drab dark grey blouse to her face and then his eyes had settled on hair that ought to have been deep gold but, unwashed as it was, it assumed the almost mousy colour of greyish brown. Linda felt colour rise in her cheeks and thought: My children always loved my hair . . . they loved to touch it, to bring it to their cheeks. 'Hello,' repeated Vasco and with a start Linda answered him.

'How do you do?' she said and held out a hand. Vasco took it and she was suddenly warm as his fingers curled unconsciously around hers.

'Clara, say hello to Mrs. Kendall.' Alice's voice was sharp and commanding.

'Hello,' a little shyly. 'I'm not going to live with my uncle. I don't like him.'

'Don't take any notice of her,' from Felix who was stepping forward, holding out his small hand. 'She's always getting told off by our uncle because she does naughty things. How do you do, Mrs. Kendall,' he added gravely as she took his hand after releasing Vasco's.

'Uncle Duarte only likes boys!' To everyone's

surprise—or perhaps Alice was not surprised—Clara pulled her tongue out as if she were doing it to her uncle.

'No such thing!' declared Alice severely. 'Don't you dare to let your uncle hear you say a thing like that or you'll be in real trouble, young lady!'

'And don't let him see you pull your tongue out,' advised Felix still in that grave manner he had used towards Linda. 'He is very cross with rudeness.'

'I shan't let him see me—but I'll do it all the same!'

'She's a forward little madam for five and a half,' observed Auntie Sal. 'She wants her bottom smacked.'

The child's enormous brown eyes took on a glassy stare.

'Don't you give any cheek,' warned Alice sternly, 'or I shall certainly give you what you deserve!'

Linda looked at each child in turn, and liked them all, but in different ways. Vasco was the one who gave the impression of strength, and he was highly intelligent. He could be mischievous, she decided, a handful. He needed a man's hand to keep him in check. Felix, though gentler and more serious of manner, was yet showing strength of character and she felt he would accept responsibility even at this early age. Clara—well, she ought to have been a boy, thought Linda. She was in fact a tomboy while at the same time Linda strongly suspected she would use her sex to get her own way, use it as a weapon against the boys should they happen to act in a way she did not like—as when Vasco was kicking the ball too hard just now.

'I'm only a girl,' she seemed to be saying, 'so just you be more considerate to me.'

She had changed her expression and now there was a mischievous sparkle in her eyes.

'No one can make me go to Uncle Duarte,' she said and all the while she was secretly admitting that what she said was carrying no weight at all. Alice, knowing her so well, summed it up very correctly indeed.

'She talks for the sake of it, and says things she hopes will annoy. She hopes to goad me into an argument but'—Alice stopped to wag a finger sternly at her—'instead, young miss, you'll get that spanking which Mrs. Smethurst said you deserved.'

Vasco broke in before his sister could speak.

'When do we have to go to Uncle's, Mrs. Kendall?'

'As soon as possible,' Alice submitted. 'His orders were that there was to be no unnecessary delay.'

'But I like the school,' inserted Clara. 'I've had two fights today and won them both.'

The two older women exchanged glances.

'The sooner the better,' said Auntie Sal with a disapproving glance at Clara. 'That one needs a man to keep an eye on her!'

Clara gave a deep sigh, and tugged at her long dark hair.

'I wish Mummy would hurry up and come back to us.'

'So do I,' from Felix. He was standing very still, looking at Linda through eyes even darker than those of his sister. His hair, like hers, was dark brown but otherwise there was little else in which they were alike. Clara's features were chubby, her mouth full-lipped but small—like a rosebud, thought Linda—very attractive. She'd be a real beauty one day. Felix's facial lines and contours were more severe; he carried the noble stamp of his mother's people, was Linda's verdict. Vasco, at only eight years of age, seemed exceptionally mature, both in his manner and his speech. Taller than his brother by about two inches, he seemed older than his age. He was springing up fast, using a great deal of energy. He would have to be watched in case he began to outgrow his strength, she decided.

'Off you go and play again.' Alice waved a hand and they obeyed at once, closing the door quietly behind them.

'Well, do you think you can manage them?' Alice inquired and Linda instantly nodded her head.

'I think I shall enjoy taking them,' she said and if she was aware of the look her aunt shot at her she chose to ignore it.

But she was glad that Auntie Sal was happy with what was taking place. She had been Linda's one and only prop, for both her parents were dead, Linda's mother having died four years ago, less than a year after her husband. And with no brothers or sisters, Linda had no one to turn to when the accident devastated her life, no one but Auntie Sal, who was a veritable giant in her support. Linda did have some in-laws but somehow she and they had never really hit it off, and so when David died the link was broken altogether. None of his family had thought to rally round his stricken widow, and now she did not want even to acknowledge them in the street—although she did force herself to do so if ever the necessity arose.

'So that's settled, my dear.' Alice was plainly relieved and as Auntie Sal was equally filled with satisfaction, Linda felt she had made the only decision possible under the circumstances.

And now that the decision *was* made she was staggered at the way she felt a lifting of the leaden weight that had lain on her for so long.

She was looking forward to something for the first time in over two years.

# Chapter Two

Linda stood on the verandah of her bedroom and stared out over the immaculate grounds of the Palacio de Dominga. Although she had been prepared for something quite out of the ordinary, she had never in her wildest dreams imagined anything as impressive as the grandeur that met her gaze immediately she had stepped from the magnificent white Rolls Royce which had brought her and the children from the airport. Flying the pennant bearing the Dominga crest, it was driven by a chauffeur in a dark blue and gold uniform that looked as if it had come straight from the tailors. His name, he said, was Ferdinand, but he had scarcely spoken this information when all the children shouted in chorus,

'Hi, Ferdy!' And then Felix added slowly, 'How is Helena-Maria?'

'My little daughter is fully recovered, Felix. It is thoughtful of you to ask about her.' The man spoke in broken English, although Linda knew that all three children spoke Portuguese fluently. He was speaking English in respect for her and somehow the act seemed to send warmth spreading through her whole body.

It had been cold and lifeless for so long. . . .

'Miss—Dom Duarte will see you now.'

Linda swung around, faintly startled as Leonor, one of the maids, came to the room behind her and stood, white-aproned and straight, in the frame of the French window.

'Thank you. . . .' She felt awkward even with the maid. 'Er—shall you conduct me to him? I'm afraid I should become lost otherwise.'

A smile like that of the Mona Lisa touched the girl's mouth.

'He said I must accompany you, miss,' she said, her English rather better than that of the chauffeur but heavily accented for all that. It amazed Linda that all these servants could speak her language. She had been met by another, older woman whom she took to be the housekeeper, a woman dignified and rather austere, but she had greeted Linda with a smile nevertheless, and had motioned Leonor to take the children up to the rooms they usually occupied when on holiday here. The older woman had taken Linda to her bedroom, an apartment of breathtaking luxury with its own dressing and bathrooms.

'Dom Duarte offers his apology at not being able to meet you himself,' she had said—and this was when a smile appeared. 'But he will see you in about half an hour's time. Meanwhile, perhaps you would like to freshen up? Your suitcase will be up directly—Adolfo will bring it.'

The manner of the woman was gracious but cool, her English impeccable. Linda had looked at herself critically in the long, silver-gilt framed mirror and a deep sigh escaped her. For although she had washed her hair it did not shine as it used to, and it seemed to hang in 'rats' tails instead of being springy and flicking up at the ends. Her face—well, she could do nothing about its sallow aspect, nor did she want to do anything about the paleness of her lips. Rouge would have improved them but she didn't even own any these days. Her dress, of dull grey jersey, had been the despair of her aunt when she had decided to buy it the day before yesterday in readiness for wearing for this trip.

There was no need for this deliberate drabness, her aunt had said, and for the first time there was an admonishing note in her voice. Linda had let it all fall on deaf ears. She had no wish to make herself attractive.

'This way, miss.' Leonor was standing aside for Linda to enter the bedroom. 'It is a nice view from your window, yes?'

'Very charming.' Linda still felt awkward and wondered how she would be feeling a few moments from now when she came face to face with the august master of the Palacio de Dominga.

Leonor led her down the wide, curving balustraded staircase and into the vast entrance hall through which she had already come. She now noticed things she had missed: the high wide archways hung with exotic plants, the tapestried walls, the ancient chests in black oak, the massive bronze urns spilling over with flowers. Persian rugs, cabinets filled with rare porcelain, ancient *azulegos*—those lovely blue and white tiles—the French furniture . . . all compounded to create an impression of great wealth, yet one of exquisite good taste as well. Linda had the impression as she passed through this great and imposing entrance hall for the second time, that although the house must be magnificent, it was a 'lived-in' home, cherished in the same way as a poor fisherman down by the shore might cherish his small cottage.

At last the room was reached and Linda was standing outside a massive door flanked by Doric-style wooden columns topped by the coat of arms of the Dominga family. She thought of Marianna and felt very sad for her.

To lose all this . . .

Leonor tapped lightly and was bidden to enter.

'Mrs. Kendall. . . .' She bobbed a curtsy and turned to leave the room.

Linda swallowed, then felt angry with herself for her nervousness. After all, she had come here on an errand and as this was now accomplished she was here merely to be interviewed, thanked, told how long she must stay, and perhaps given her wages—or part of them.

'Do sit down.' The cultured voice was low and faintly accented.

She took possession of the chair, sitting right on the edge and taking a swift, surreptitious glance around her.

The room was a study of massive proportions, with a huge Regency desk, its tooled top of red leather almost covered with ledgers and files and other evidence of the work that went on here. As owner of one of the districts largest *quintas,* Dom Duarte had masses of paper work to attend to and Alice had mentioned that he did it all himself. He employed an estate manager but all the 'office work' was carried out by Dom Duarte, its being traditional in the family. His father and grandfather had run the *quinta* in the same way.

'You had a good flight, Mrs. Kendall?' His voice brought her eyes to his face. She had been admiring the crimson walls with their embossed satin covering, the Aubusson carpet, the crystal chandeliers—rare Waterford antiques, she was later to learn.

'Yes, thank you, Mr.—er—Dom Duarte.' She felt the hot blood flow into her cheeks, tinting them with colour. This man was so magnificent that she felt she ought to be addressing him as 'Your Majesty'! His features were clear-cut, chiselled in aristocratic lines, his skin smooth and dark as well-matured teak. The mouth was firm yet sensual, the eyes, framed by long thick lashes, seemed almost black but were in fact charcoal grey with metallic glints; the fact that they were so deep-set made them appear darker, she realised. He had black hair inclined to wave against a wide, unlined forehead, thick hair, gleaming with cleanness and health.

Unconsciously Linda drew a hand through her own hair, hotly conscious of all that it lacked.

Yet why should she suddenly care what she looked like? Not for over two years had she bothered even to make herself presentable, for she was merely existing—certainly not living.

She was conscious of Dom Duarte's stare, his critical examination. Auntie Sal had said that she looked well over thirty, she recalled, and that was before she had donned the drab grey jersey wool dress—well, it wasn't wool, but a man-made fibre which, declared Auntie Sal, made it appear even more drab than it would had it been made of some decent material.

'I'm sorry I couldn't have met you immediately on your arrival,' he was saying. 'I had things to do.' That was all; she guessed that he would not bother with explanations, especially to an employee, which was in effect what she was. 'However, we can now have a little chat. I believe Mrs. Sutherland did mention to you that I would wish you to stay on with the children for a while?'

I would wish . . . Not I hope you will stay on, or would you mind staying on? No, an order . . . Linda was more concerned, however, with the words 'for a while.'

She said, looking at him,

'How long would you want me to stay? I understood it would be only for a few days.'

He was shaking his head even before she had finished speaking. And his mouth was set in that kind of a line which made Linda distinctly uneasy.

'I want you to stay until I get someone suitable,

and that won't be an easy or a quick matter. I have to advertise, as the agency in town can't help me. I have already consulted them, naturally, but with no success.' He was tapping a blotter idly with a gold paper knife. 'You are not in employment, I understand?'

'No, but—'

'In that case there seems to be no problem. You will be in my employ as the children's nanny—'

'Dom Duarte—'

'Mrs. Kendall,' he said in a very soft tone, 'I am not used to being interrupted. Please remember that in future. And now, there is the question of your salary. If the sum I have in mind is unsuitable then say so at once.' He mentioned the salary; Linda's eyes widened to their greatest extent and she thought that if money had had any importance in her life then she would be wanting the post to go on indefinitely!

But money meant nothing to her and she merely said,

'I can't stay more than a week, Dom Duarte. I'm sorry.'

The fine eyebrows came together in a frown.

'A week? Is there some reason why you can't stay longer?'

'I live with my aunt,' she began, then stopped, feeling foolish because she had no idea what else she had to say. She rather thought that Auntie Sal would welcome being on her own for a while.

'Mrs. Sutherland did mention that. But she also mentioned that you weren't doing anything much at the present time—' He stopped and hesitated as if debating on whether or not to say what was in his mind. However, she was soon hearing him speak again, in that most attractive foreign voice with its faint hint of an accent. 'I believe you have had a tragedy in your life?'

She looked down at her hands. Her lips moved convulsively but it was some moments before she could articulate words. When she did her voice was rough and husky with emotion.

'Yes, I lost my husband and two children in a car accident.'

There was a small silence; she glanced up to see a dark face shaded with compassion.

'I hadn't realised it was as bad as that,' he said presently. 'Mrs. Sutherland didn't say much—merely that you'd had a bereavement.' He paused a moment. 'How old were your children?' he then asked.

'Three—they—they were twins—a boy and a girl. . . .' She was on the edge of tears and half rose from the chair. 'I'm sorry—I had better go—'

'No; sit down, Mrs. Kendall. Collect yourself for a few minutes. I have some phone calls to make which I shall do in another room.' With that he rose from behind the desk and quietly left the room.

Within five minutes or so Leonor came in carrying a silver tray on which was a small silver tea set and some delicate china—a cup and saucer and a plate. Beneath a silver cover was a hot buttered muffin which smelled so delicious that despite how she was feeling Linda just had to eat it. Leonor had obviously received specific orders, for once she had poured a cup of tea and uncovered the muffin she turned and went out.

The Conde was austere to look at, forbidding in that his noble features were stern, with that kind of look that makes one feel he would be immovable once he had made up his mind about anything. He had an air of sheer arrogance about him, too, and yet . . . he could be kind.

On his return she was able to produce a smile, albeit a thin one, but yet it brought a look of approval. His dark eyes rested for a space on the tray.

'Was the tea to your liking?' he inquired and she nodded immediately.

'It was lovely. I enjoyed it. Thank you.' She was awkward again, uncomfortable in his presence.

'And have you changed your mind about the post I am offering?'

She paused. It seemed the height of ungraciousness to decline the offer now that he had been so kind to her.

'Can I think about it and give you my answer in the morning?' she queried at last.

'If that is what you want.' His voice had a crisp edge to it which for some quite incomprehensible reason hurt her a little.

'I feel I must think about it.' Linda's voice was low and apologetic. 'You see, I hadn't expected to be asked to stay any longer than a few days—a week at the most.'

'Your aunt, with whom you live—will she mind very much if you stay until I find someone suitable?'

'I feel she won't mind at all.' Linda, her awkwardness dissolving somewhat, explained about her aunt and how she liked to live alone. 'Perhaps,' ended Linda feeling she was being driven by some force beyond her control, 'I shall decide to stay—just for a while.'

'That's fine.' He seemed to think it was settled because he added briskly, 'And the salary? It suits you?'

'It's too much—' The statement was out before she realised it and she saw the hint of an amused smile touch the fine outline of his mouth.

'Mrs. Kendall, that is the first time any prospective employee has ever said a thing like that to me.' He rose from the chair which he had occupied after re-entering the study. 'It's settled, then. You will be shown the suite which the children will occupy and where they will take their lessons—'

'Lessons—' The interruption came out before she had time to suppress it and she was swift to offer an apology, colouring up at the same time.

'I do not expect you to give them anything complicated. They must have some lessons, though, if only to keep them out of mischief. I shall get some books brought in and so you should have no difficulty in giving them some elementary instruction in the simple maths they are used to doing, and whatever else—' He broke off, flicking a hand impatiently. 'I leave it to you, Mrs. Kendall.'

She was in her room when Leonor came to say that she would show her the suite the children were to occupy. It was plain that although there were many maids in the Palacio the Conde was using only Leonor to look after Linda and for this she was grateful since she would be able to get used to the girl and in consequence lose her awkwardness.

'Thank you. Where are the children now?' It was barely ten minutes since she had left Dom Duarte's study, and less than an hour since she had arrived at the Palacio.

'Dom Duarte said they are not to trouble you today, miss, so Tereza is looking after them. She will see to their evening meal and put them to bed. They are used to her because they have visited here with their mother several times. Tereza is my sister and she has worked here for a year longer than I.'

'And how long have you been working here?' The question was put merely for the sake of making conversation as Linda followed the Portuguese girl from the bedroom onto the wide gallery from which one could look down on to the great entrance hall.

'Four years. I am very happy. Dom Duarte is good to us all.' She stopped eventually at a high wide door and opened it. 'There are three bedrooms, a sitting-room and a schoolroom—oh, and there are bathrooms with each bedroom, of course.' She was opening one door after another as she spoke. Linda, having entered in her wake, just stood and stared. 'It's the Nursery Suite,' explained Leonor. 'At one time it was much larger because the family had many more children than they do these days.'

'Much larger?'

'There were another four bedrooms.'

'Has Dom Duarte any brothers and sisters—other than the children's mother, I mean?' Linda had no idea why she put the question.

'He has two brothers and one sister. Their names are Juan and Diaz and Inez.'

'They're all younger, of course?'

'His brothers are—Juan is twenty-eight and Diaz a year younger, but Inez is thirty-two and she is married with two children—' The girl stopped abruptly, which caused Linda to glance sharply at her. The pretty face was set, the brown eyes glinting. 'They come to stay sometimes,' continued Leonor at length. 'Always at Christmas they come —all the family of a great *fidalgo* comes to his home at Christmas. We make much of it in Portugal.'

'*Fidalgo?*' echoed Linda. 'What does that mean exactly?'

'That is what a great nobleman is called.'

'I see. . . .' For the first time in two years Linda was finding herself interested in something. 'And Christmas is a very special time here in Portugal, you say?'

'Yes. You will not be here for Christmas?'

Linda shook her head.

'No; I'm staying only until Dom Duarte gets a nanny for the children.'

The girl grimaced.

'It takes a long time, and maybe the children's mother will be out of hospital before he manages to get anybody.' She closed the door she was holding and looked at her. 'If you can, you might as well stay.'

'You sound as if you'd like me to.'

A smile lit the girl's eyes.

'I would. I very much like English people. I hope one day to visit your country.'

'I shall invite you when I am in my own home again and settled.'

'In your own home, miss?'

Linda bit her lip, staggered that she had been able to talk to this girl, a stranger, like this. It was as though the change of scene and environment had loosened up some tightness which had seized her on the day of the tragedy and never eased since.

'I live with an aunt at present,' she said at last. 'But soon I shall return to my own house.' She smiled thinly at the girl. 'I'll keep my promise,' she said.

'That will be lovely! I shall look forward to it.'

'The three children are sleeping in there to-night?' Linda was asking when eventually Leonor was leaving her, outside her own room.

The girl shook her head.

'No; they usually sleep in the south wing and Dom Duarte's put them there for tonight, just in case they are upset by the disruption in their lives. But tomorrow they'll be moving into the Nursery Suite.'

Linda would have liked to go in and say good night to the children but she could not bring herself to ask and so she went back to her room, wondering where she was supposed to eat. Not that she was hungry; she never was these days, but her aunt had insisted on her eating regularly, with dinner being served at around eight o'clock.

To her surprise and dismay Leonor came back about half an hour later to say that the Conde had invited her to take dinner with him.

'Oh. . . .' Linda stemmed the refusal in time; she had no wish to reveal embarrassment before the girl. 'I—er—haven't brought anything suitable for dining,' she did add, feeling this might make an adequate enough excuse.

'He did say that perhaps you would be too tired to change, miss, and so he wouldn't change either.' The girl's expression revealed nothing of her thoughts. 'That dress will be all right, I'm sure.'

Just what had been said? Linda wondered, then decided that the Conde would be quite adept at conveying a meaning in the most subtle way possible, if the necessity arose.

'Very well. Does Dom Duarte want me to come down now?'

'He said in about twenty minutes to half an hour, miss.'

'Thank you.' Linda paused. 'I'll not find my way—'

'It's the room two doors down the hall from the study which you were in.'

'On the same side?' There had seemed to be a bewildering number of doors off the main hall.

'That's right, miss.'

When she had gone Linda found herself making a critical assessment of her appearance. David, her adoring husband, wouldn't recognise her, she thought, and a great flood of depression swept over her like a deluge. Suddenly she wanted to look nice. The knowledge staggered her and she asked herself the reason for this change. There was no valid explanation except the one of the change of scene—which was scarcely an explanation at all, she very soon was admitting.

Whatever, she looked at the two dresses she had brought with her and which were now hanging in the massive wardrobe, looking rather lost. She had brought a white silk blouse as well, and a midnight blue calf-length skirt in soft pan velvet. She'd had no intention of bringing these two articles but her aunt had insisted on putting them in the suitcase.

'I'll not need anything like that,' Linda had protested.

'You don't know, child. In any case, you can't take this thing empty!'

'It isn't going to be empty.' Linda had at that very moment been putting in her nightdress and some underwear. 'I shall take two dresses and that's all I shall need, besides the one I'll be wearing, that is.'

Her aunt had continued to argue until in the end Linda decided it was simpler to let her have her own way. It wasn't as if the blouse and skirt added much weight to the case.

Now, she took them out and laid them on the bed, her body tensed, immobile at the idea of breaking the habit of two years. . . .

With a glance at her wristwatch she knew she had little time to make up her mind. And perhaps it was this which did in fact force her decision. She took off the jersey dress, had a quick shower, put on her underwear, and over it the blouse and skirt.

She stood before the mirror again. The blouse hung a little loosely now, because of the weight she had lost, and the waistband of the skirt was also loose. However, she managed to fix it with a safety-pin and there was no doubt that the outfit looked charming, and flattering even though her face was so sallow. Suddenly she wished she had some lip rouge and a blusher.

Leonor tapped on the door at that very moment and entered in response to Linda's 'come in.'

'I forgot to tell you that I'll bring your morning tea when you ring the bell. That's it, by the far side of the bed.'

Linda frowned.

'I don't want you to bring me tea in bed,' she said.

'It's the Conde's orders, miss.'

'I see. . . .' She didn't see at all as a matter of fact. She was only a servant like Leonor, so why should she be waited on?

'Is there anything you want, miss?' Her eyes were running over Linda's figure and there was an unfathomable expression on her face. Linda squirmed inwardly at the idea of what the girl might be thinking: that she, Linda, was endeavouring to look attractive . . . for the Conde. . . .

'No, nothing,' she replied.

'You look pretty, miss—if you don't mind my saying so?'

'Not at all. I felt I ought to change into something—er—cooler. It's very warm, don't you think?'

'Just right for me.' A small pause and then, 'You're pale, miss. Have you been ill?'

'Not ill, Leonor,' she replied.

'Are you going to make-up?'

A frown knit Linda's brow.

'No, of course not. In any case,' she added without thinking, 'I haven't any make-up with me.'

'You forgot it? What a shame. But I have some I could lend you—it hasn't been used. A friend bought it for me and it's not really my colour. The blusher's more for a fairer complexion.'

Well, thought Linda grimly, mine's not fair these days. It's just a nondescript sallow.

And then she heard herself say,

'I'd not borrow it, Leonor, but if it's unsuitable for you and it's for my colouring then I'll buy it from you and you can replace it with the right colour.' She glanced at her watch as she spoke and discovered that she had only five minutes to the half hour which Leonor had mentioned.

'I'll run and get it!'

The girl was back within sixty seconds. Breathlessly she said,

'I don't want to sell it, miss—'

'I can't take it, then.'

'Please do—oh, well, we'll talk about the price tomorrow. I hope you have a nice evening, miss. Good night,' she thought to add over her shoulder as she reached the door.

'Good night, Leonor.' Linda watched the door

close, then looked down at the box in her hand. She opened the lid. A full range . . . lip rouge, blusher, eye shadow, mascara. . . .

Slowly she closed the lid and, walking over to the dressing table, she laid the box down.

Then she brushed her hair, fastened it back with a small slide . . . and her eyes strayed to the box again. . . .

# Chapter Three

She supposed it was natural that the Conde's eyes should flicker with surprise when she entered the dining room where he was standing by the window, his tall frame silhouetted against flaring lights illuminating the courtyard outside, with its mimosas and jacarandas, its fountains and its masses of exotic flowers. He had turned with a slow and fluid movement, and there was no indication of his surprise other than that faint flicker of the deep-set, dark grey eyes. She noticed the outthrust chin, the firm mouth above it, the straight classical line of the nose—the entire face, in fact, which seemed to draw her in some indefinable way that both puzzled and excited her. Not for two whole years had any man's attractions had any effect on her . . . but now . . .

Vaguely she knew she had gone to all this trouble

with her appearance just for him, and although she knew a certain disloyalty to her husband's memory, all that seemed important at this moment was that the Conde should not despise her for looking drab.

A slow smile dissolved some of the austerity but not all; it was an inherent part of him, passed on from a long line of exalted ancestors.

'You look rested,' he observed and she thought that only a man like the Conde could be so very subtle in his comment on the change in her appearance. 'Would you care for a drink?' he inquired, his dark eyes sweeping over her again from head to foot. He had indicated a chair by the window, a low, beautiful upholstered chair in French tapestry. She realised that the room was in two parts, one being the dining-area and the other, much smaller, the 'lounge' where aperitifs or other drinks were usually taken when there were no large numbers of guests to be catered for. All was, therefore, intimate, and this atmosphere was made even more intimate by the flowers spilling from crystal vases, from a lovely wall container in Sevres porcelain, and from a hanging basket in which almond blossom had been placed along with the delicate, ornamental greenery that grew permanently in it. The lights were concealed beneath the pelmets of the long Italian brocatelle drapes which at present were wide open, as was the window, allowing the scents of the gardens to drift in. Soft music from four inconspicuous speakers overtoned the gentle sough of the breeze. On the dining table two silver-gilt candelabra, each with five branches, held the kind of candles Linda had often admired in shops like Harrods but had never been able to buy. The wineglasses gleamed as did the silver cutlery. Hand-embroidered table linen from Madeira, immaculately laundered, lent colour, as did the flower arrangements at each end of the table and at each cover.

She answered him after this swift glance around.

'Just a dry martini, please.'

He poured it for her; she noticed his clothes, the casual, blouson-type fawn jacket over mid-brown slacks. His shirt looked like pure silk which had been stiffened; it was off-white and the tie was the same colour as the slacks.

'You're very quiet,' he remarked after sitting down on a chair opposite to her and hitching up a trouser leg.

She felt herself colouring up. Her feelings were confused, for on the one hand she wished she were back in her bedroom, and yet on the other she knew a strange, inexplicable desire to be able to talk to him . . . to open up her heart and mind as it had never been opened up since that fateful moment when, on going to her front door, she had seen the policeman standing there, his face twisted by the news he had to impart to her. Yes, she had been tight inside for too long; her aunt had tried to loosen the knots which pain and loss had tied within her but much as she loved Auntie Sal, and grateful as she was to her, Linda could in no way open up and reveal what was inside her.

She said in answer to his comment,

'I was—surprised at—at your invitation.' She

was conscious of the colour entering more deeply into her cheeks. 'I'd expected to—well, to eat in the kitch—er—somewhere else.'

If he noticed her stammering awkwardness he mercifully ignored it and spoke at once, as if he would put her at her ease. Assuredly he was a compassionate man, she thought—this despite the strong suspicion that, conversely, he could be hard to the point of ruthlessness if ever anyone should cross him.

'I felt you'd be feeling strange, and a little lost,' he said in that foreign voice that was beginning to have an effect on her which she was totally unable to describe. 'The tragedy is plainly still with you, and it was not good that you be alone this evening. I hope,' he ended with the hint of a smile, 'that you will enjoy your meal.'

Her mouth had begun to move convulsively when he mentioned the tragedy but now she managed to respond to his smile.

'I'm sure I shall, Dom Duarte. . . .' Her eyes were wide and limpid as they met his. 'And thank you for—for your kindness in asking me to—to dine with you.'

To that he made no comment, but sat looking at the amber liquid in his glass, his eyes thoughtful and faintly mysterious; his lips were pursed and Linda felt he had drifted a long way from her, that an idea, still vague, had entered his mind.

The first course was brought in by a manservant, Vitor, who was about to serve his employer first but the flick of a hand sent him to the other side of the table. Linda was served smoked salmon on a thin bed of crisp lettuce with other garnishings to add colour and interest. She looked across at her handsome companion and waited until he was served before taking up her knife and fork.

The Conde soon opened a conversation, and once again Linda experienced this urge to talk about herself. The opportunity did not at this stage arise, as he was commenting on the varying qualities of the children's characters. She had to smile when he declared that Clara was a tomboy.

'She might just be a handful for you,' he added. 'She's as mercurial as quicksilver. However, if you have any trouble you must call on me. Clara knows better than to try my patience.'

'I daresay all three children are missing their mother, though, and that could affect their behaviour.'

'They miss their father, too.' He spoke in a hard, brittle tone. 'You know all the circumstances, of course?'

She nodded her head.

'Mrs. Sutherland did tell me a few things. It's sad that they have no father any more.'

The Conde allowed that to pass without comment.

'Felix,' he said musingly. 'He's going to be the brilliant one. Rather too serious for a young child, but not without spirit, nevertheless. Vasco of course is always conscious of being the eldest and for that reason he needs rather stricter treatment than the others.' He glanced at her and added, 'Here again, if you have trouble you must come to me.'

She nodded, but absently. Linda could not imagine herself running to the Conde with complaints. Besides, she wanted the confidence and friendship of the children and tale-carrying on her part would do nothing to assist the building up of that kind of rapport.

'How long do you think I shall be here?' she ventured when they were sitting back waiting for the fish course to be served.

'There isn't any hurry for you to leave.' A statement, which left her without anything to say. It struck her that *he* was in no hurry for her to leave the Palacio! 'The children like you— Oh, yes, I have spoken with them in order to discover their feelings. They were very happy when Mrs. Sutherland was looking after them, and my sister believed they would never take to anyone else, hence her decision not to employ anyone to take her place. But looking after them was too much for her and when she eventually returns to her home here she will require a nanny.'

Linda's eyes darted to his. What exactly was he telling her? She said slowly,

'You did mention that you would be looking for a nanny, and that once you found a suitable one I could leave.'

His mouth seemed to tighten but his tone was friendly enough when he spoke.

'I don't see why you are so anxious to leave, Mrs. Kendall. From what I have gathered you have nothing to occupy your mind back home and that is not good—' He shook his head knowingly. 'In order to recover from the kind of experience you

49

have suffered you must find something to take your thoughts away from it—'

'But I don't want to forget. . . .' Her voice trailed as she realised that once again she had interrupted him. She was about to murmur an apology but he spoke first.

'Are you telling me that you enjoy dwelling on the tragedy?' He did not give her time to answer as he added with a sudden frown, 'Enjoy is not of course the correct word. You are more content—shall we say—in brooding, than you would be if you found yourself managing to have moments—perhaps hours—of forgetfulness?'

Linda averted her eyes.

'I expect,' she murmured, 'that you think I'm morbid?'

'Not at all.' The accent seemed somehow rather more noticeable than before. 'I have a certain understanding of your emotions, Mrs. Kendall, but although I can sympathise I also know that, with some kind of effort, you yourself can ease the pain and that eventually you will be able, in many ways, to enjoy your life again.'

She could only stare, bewildered by his gravity, his gentleness; and more than anything was she puzzled by the unmistakable emphasis on the word 'know.'

How did he *know?*

She hadn't time to speak before he was saying,

'The life you will lead here, with the children, the change in scenery and so many things besides, will take your mind off your loss—' He waved an imperative hand when she made to interrupt and soft colour tinted her cheeks. 'You must give yourself a chance,' he went on almost sternly now. 'How old are you?' he inquired unexpectedly.

'Twenty-six—almost twenty-seven.'

Not by the flicker of an eyelid did he express surprise. He said quietly,

'You were determined to let yourself grow old quickly, weren't you?'

'Yes, I was,' she admitted.

'Yesterday you looked all of thirty-five.' He sounded heartless, she thought, and wondered where the compassion had gone.

'I know—my aunt was always telling me to—to try,' she ended with a sigh.

'But when one feels one has nothing left to live for one is apt to let oneself go.' He paused and she thought: he has the most uncanny understanding of my situation. 'It's a natural reaction,' he went on at once. 'But it mustn't go on and on until you're old. You have much to live for, and remember—' Again he paused, this time to stare directly at her. 'Others have suffered losses and managed to live again.'

She nodded in mute agreement. And for several minutes all was silence as Vitor served the next course. Dom Duarte poured the wine, one of his own specials, he had told her, the grapes being grown on the valleyside where the mineral contents of the soil were excellent for the properties of the wine.

'I do realise that others have suffered as I have,' she said when eventually they were alone again.

'But it seems disloyal to my husband's memory—and to my lovely children—if I forget, and begin to enjoy my life again. Oh, it is so difficult to make people understand!' she cried, vainly trying to hide her distress. 'The truth is that I *can't* forget, even if I wanted to!'

'Of course you can't forget,' he agreed and now his voice was gentle again, compassionate. 'You never will, not as long as you live. But you can help yourself to forget the actual pain.'

'You mean—that I shall be able to remember without having any pain?' She shook her head because it seemed impossible.

'That's exactly what I do mean,' he said. 'The day can come when you can think about those loved ones—and undoubtedly you often will do so—but there will be no pain, just memories of the happy times you all had together.' He sounded faraway all at once, yet his eyes were on her, and there was deep kindness and understanding in their depths. 'Think about what I have said,' he advised her, 'and try—just try, and keep on trying.'

For a while there was silence, a sort of intimate, companionable silence, while they ate the delicious roast duckling in orange sauce. A confection of fruit and cream came next and then they moved to the other end of the room for coffee and liqueurs.

The Conde had changed the subject and Linda was learning something about the *quinta*—the vineyards on the hillsides, the extensive orchards where citrus fruits were grown in vast quantities, the fields where wheat and barley were cultivated. He mentioned the cork-oak forests and explained that some of the *azulegos* she would see when she explored the house depicted the cork-oak workers and others employed on the estate, such as the treading of the grapes. She had shown curiosity about the *azulegos* and was told that they were almost always blue, and were beautifully glazed.

'You will see *azulegos* on all kinds of buildings,' he told her. 'We love to decorate with them.'

She had found herself asking about such things as weather, and flora and fauna.

'We have all the flowers which you have,' he told her. 'Plus some others as well. Our poinsettias are magnificent, as are our magnolias and camellias. They grow well here. Moon-flowers too grow over great expanses, and also geraniums.' He told her of the trees—eucalyptus and cypresses and many other forest trees.

And of course the olives and the figs which grew in the *quinta*'s orchards.

As Dom Duarte talked Linda found herself relaxing in a way she would never have believed possible. It was not just her mind, but her body too, and it dawned on her that even her muscles had become tensed. She now felt at ease, and the tragedy had, for the time, been put into the dark recesses of her subconscious. It was as if a miracle were taking place, performed by her companion, a stranger until a few hours ago. She seemed to bask in a new peace and when later she examined the situation, and the temporary divestment of her sorrow, she could only conclude that—amazing

and impossible as it might seem—there existed
some kind of a bond between the illustrious owner
of the Quinta de Dominga and herself!

She now watched him as he poured a Grand
Marnier for her and a Napolean for himself, and
marvelled at what must surely be a dual personality. For he was all arrogance and superiority at this
moment, his proud head—set on equally proud
shoulders—held erect so that above his shirt collar
the muscles of his throat stood out.

He brought the drink to her. Vitor had poured
the coffee and left the room.

He said, after taking possession of a chair and
leaning comfortably against the thick, duck down
cushions,

'Can you bring yourself to tell me something
about your husband and children, Mrs. Kendall?'
and she knew without any doubt at all that the
previous talk had not only been designed to draw
her thoughts from her grief, but also as a leader to
what he was suggesting now.

'I think so, yes,' she replied without very much
hesitation at all. For this was what she had wanted
. . . and it seemed that the man knew! His insight
was as exceptional as his superlative personality.

'You were married young?' The words provided
the opening she needed.

'I was twenty and my husband two years older.'
She stopped as she noticed his expression. His lips
moved and he seemed to be murmuring to himself,

'Twenty-two. . . .'

'A year later our twins were born. We were so
thrilled.'

'You didn't mind the extra work of having two babies instead of one?'

She shook her head and her eyes shone for the first time since the accident.

'No, not at all. David helped me all the time. It was lovely having the two growing up together.'

'You didn't want any more?' His interest seemed to increase as the question was asked.

'We did, yes, but—' She shrugged a little self-deprecatingly. 'None came along.'

'The loss must have been devastating. It's two years ago, you said?'

'Yes, just under two years.'

'So the anniversary is soon?' Dom Duarte's face was a mask.

She nodded and speech was difficult.

'In a month—the eighteenth of June, so it's less than a month.'

'You mustn't dwell on it,' he said and his eyes were hard and stern. 'I shall expect you to give much of your time to the children.'

He changed the subject before she could speak, and a short while later she was in effect being dismissed as he said, rising from his chair,

'You must be very tired. I feel sure you'll sleep.' He watched her get up from the chair. 'Good night, Mrs. Kendall. Leonor will bring up your breakfast. Dona Clementina will tell you what your full duties are—Dona Clementina is my housekeeper. You've already met her, of course.'

'Yes . . . good night, Dom Duarte.'

'Sleep well.'

She sent him a thin smile and moved to the door

which he was holding open for her. Their eyes met as she came abreast of him and lifted her face. Some inexplicable flicker of emotion stole over her; she felt a tingling of nerves that was as bewildering as it was disturbing.

Just what was happening to her?

# Chapter Four

For a long while Linda sat on her bed, dwelling on what had happened in such a short space of time. For less than twenty-four hours ago she was in her own bed, in her aunt's home in England. The sort of a home thousands of widows, living on little more than a pension, were residing in. It was a neat semi-detached house with three bedrooms, one bathroom and the usual two entertaining rooms on the ground floor. A medium-sized garden front and back, a shed in which to keep the tools. And the view? Houses all alike to the front and back. The road; and if you were one of the few fortunate ones—as Auntie Sal was—you had the park not too far away.

Yes, that was Linda's life after she had agreed to live with her aunt, who had done everything for her, the important task being that of putting Linda's special possessions into boxes and having them taken to be stored in the third bedroom of Auntie Sal's home, and then the putting of the detached house into the hands of an agent who had seen to the letting of it to reliable tenants.

And now, within those few eventful hours, here she was, Linda Kendall, living in a palatial mansion in Portugal, ancestral home of one of the country's wealthiest noblemen. A Count, no less!

And not only was she here, but it seemed very much on the cards that she could stay just as long as she liked.

At last she rose and began to undress. Her hair was still dull but the vigorous washing and brushing had done wonders. It could soon be beautiful again, she mused. Her eyes were thoughtful as she took off the blouse and skirt. Dom Duarte had said that earlier she had looked thirty-five. But now . . . ? She still looked older than her twenty-six years but certainly the clothes and the make-up had taken at least five years from those ten. Thirty. . . . Did she really look as old as the Conde? He, though, with those few attractive threads of silver at his temples, looked rather older than his age— thirty next birthday Alice had said.

Her thoughts went to the woman whom Mrs. Sutherland had mentioned: Dona Lucia Mendes, whom everyone expected the Conde to marry. What was she like? wondered Linda, who for no tangible reason felt a sort of sinking sensation stealing into her. The girl was beautiful according to Mrs. Sutherland, and Linda's eyes lifted to the mirror to make an even more critical examination of their owner's face.

With a sigh Linda went to the bathroom, turned on the gold-plated taps and ran a bath of water. Provided were several expensive brands of bath salts and foam and body oil. Leonor had brought them—from a store of such things, surmised Linda. Any guests at the Palacio would be well supplied with all their needs.

After the bath she felt better, her depression having lifted. She recalled all that the Conde had said, and with a firm resolve she decided to heed it. She would need a great deal of will-power to put her grief away—and she was convinced that in any case it could never be for very long at a time—and concentrate on other things, but she would certainly make an effort.

It was a week later and Linda was telephoning her aunt. Dom Duarte had told her to use the phone just whenever she liked, but this was the first time she had taken advantage of his offer.

'You sound cheerful, love.' Her aunt's voice sounded very close. 'I expect you are getting ready to come home. Have you enjoyed it there?'

'I'm happier than for a long time,' was all that Linda would say. 'Auntie—the Conde wants me to stay for a while, and I've agreed. I know you won't mind.'

'Mind? I'm delighted! How long does he want you to stay?'

'It was supposed to be until he found a suitable nanny for the children. But now—well, he seems to want *me* to stay with them.' Linda was not sure of this, but as far as she knew the Conde had not been making any effort to find a permanent nanny for the children.

'Until their mother comes out of hospital, you mean? And returns to Portugal?'

Linda hesitated, then divulged what had been in her mind for several days.

'To tell the truth, Auntie Sal, I have gained the impression that he doesn't want me to leave here, that he would like me to stay on and look after the children—indefinitely.'

'So you're to be a permanent nanny?'

'It's only a conclusion I have come to. Dom Duarte hasn't said specifically that he wants me to be a permanent nanny.' Yet he certainly had given the impression that he wanted her to stay. . . . Linda was confused but of course she did not mention this to her aunt who in any case was speaking, advising Linda to consider staying on at the Palacio.

'I had your letter this morning,' she continued. 'The money he's giving you as wages is marvellous! You know I shall miss you, of course, but you also know I love to be on my own. . . .' The old lady's voice trailed inexplicably and Linda was sure the cause was something that had come into her aunt's mind, something she did not like. Could it be that Auntie Sal had changed, and that she was no longer totally happy living by herself? She was speaking again, 'Just suit yourself, love. Do what you think is best. You certainly seem to have brightened up a bit.'

'It's having the children; they're so lively—well, Vasco and Clara are. Felix—he needs attention in a different way, being a rather serious-minded child, yet fun for all that.'

'Seems a very charming boy.'

'They're all charming in their own particular ways.'

There was a slight pause before Auntie Sal said,

'I expect that if you do decide to take on the permanent post you'll be living elsewhere—I mean, Marianna is sure to want her own home, especially if the Conde is thinking of getting married, as Alice believes.'

'She's said something to you recently?' A wave of something akin to actual nausea suddenly affected Linda's being.

'She corresponds with one of the Conde's maids, an older woman of about her own age. Helena, I think she said her name was. Have you met her?'

'Yes. She's the one immediately under the housekeeper. Very bossy with the younger maids, from what I've seen, but very nice to me, of course.'

'Well, this is the one who supplies the information and she wrote to Alice a few days ago and said an engagement might be announced shortly. You might find yourself caught up in a wedding if you stay. It should be exciting—the wedding of a Count. Think of all the Portuguese nobility who'll be there.'

'I don't think I sh-shall stay that long, Auntie, after all.' Linda's voice was hoarse.

'But—'

'I did imply just now that I hadn't quite made up my mind.'

'I hope you'll stay, dear. You do need this complete change of environment. You're away from painful reminders of what happened. And those children—they must be keeping your mind off other things, surely?'

'They are.' Linda paused a moment. 'I'll think about it, Auntie. I do know how you love to be on your own.'

'But if you do come back, Linda, this home is yours, you know that.'

'Of course I do.'

'Have you met the Conde's intended yet?'

The Conde's intended. . . . What kind of emotion was this which she was feeling?

'No, I haven't, but she comes to dinner this evening with her brother so perhaps I shall catch a glimpse of her.'

'She lives close by? Alice never mentioned where she lives.'

'I think Mrs. Sutherland did say that the two estates join, if you remember, Auntie.'

'Ah, yes, I do remember now you mention it. Yes, of course, Alice said it would be a very good match because the two estates will be joined.'

'Dom Duarte's estate is vast as it is.' Linda could not explain what brought forth this remark.

'But these wealthy millionaire landowners always want to increase their possessions.'

'Yes,' flatly, 'I expect they do, Auntie.'

'I'm going to see Alice this evening. She's having

a little supper party for her birthday. Just seven of us going.'

'That should be nice. Wish her many happy returns from me—and thank her for choosing me for this assignment, won't you?' Linda did not wait for her aunt to reply as she added, 'How old is Mrs. Sutherland?'

'Don't know; she's close regarding her age. As a matter of fact, she's close about a lot of things. She's never said much at all about the man you're now working for, or his sister. Still, I suppose that when you work for that kind of person you have to respect the fact that they wouldn't want you to discuss their private affairs. But I've always been a bit curious about the people she worked for, and especially the Conde, whom she obviously knows fairly well, having visited the Palacio so often.'

'Well, there isn't anything more I can think of to talk about,' said Linda a few minutes later when the conversation had begun to flag. 'Dom Duarte was kind to let me phone you so I mustn't stay on too long.'

'No, of course not, love. I'll answer your letter in a day or so. Meanwhile, take care of yourself—and do give serious thought to stopping on as a permanent nanny. Apart from anything else the money's excellent.'

'Yes. . . .' Linda added goodbye and hung up.

Dom Duarte was behind her as she began to move away, his having come from his study.

'I have been ringing my aunt,' she felt obliged to explain.

'That's all right. You must use the phone whenever you like. Don't feel cut off from your aunt when there isn't any need.'

She smiled and thanked him. His gaze was prolonged and curious. Perhaps, she thought, he was thinking that her smiles came rather more often than when first she arrived here.

Was it only a mere eight days that she had been here? It seemed much longer, for she had fitted in wonderfully well, and a friendly relationship existed between her and the housekeeper, and all the other servants for that matter. But Leonor would always be Linda's favourite. The girl was bright and cheerful, always wanting to know if there was anything she could do. It was as if she understood, but of course she knew nothing of Linda's background; no one did except the Conde.

He was speaking, and it did seem that he had been carefully considering before he said,

'I'd like you to dine with me again this evening, Mrs. Kendall. I believe you will know that I have two friends dining with me, and you can make the foursome.'

'Me!' Taken aback, she could only stand there, staring blankly and shaking her head. 'I couldn't,' she managed at last.

'And why?' Dom Duarte's tone was crisp.

'I—because—' She broke off and spread her hands in a little helpless gesture. 'I haven't the right kind of dress,' she added almost on a note of triumph and the ghost of a smile curved the sensuous outline of his mouth.

'That can be taken care of,' the Conde assured her suavely.

Again she shook her head.

'I—I would feel—embarrassed with strangers,' she told him desperately.

'No such thing. Dona Lucia and her brother Felipe are very friendly people whom you will like immediately you are introduced to them. And now, about the dress—'

'I can't!' interrupted Linda still in the same desperate way.

'Mrs. Kendall,' said the Conde in a firm and rather chilly accent, 'it was an order, not a request.'

'An—order, Dom Duarte?'

He inclined his head.

'I have need of a fourth at my dinner table. You will oblige me by performing the duty. And now about the dress,' he said again. 'There are several boutiques in town where you can purchase all you'll need. The account will be sent to me.'

'Dom Duarte—'

She was abruptly silenced by an imperious lift of his hand.

'No argument, please,' he warned in a very soft voice. 'My wishes are paramount.' He looked down into her anxious face, perhaps seeking for signs of anger but Linda was far too gripped by apprehension to feel anger. 'There is absolutely nothing to fear,' he added a little more kindly. 'You dined with me on your first evening here and you felt quite comfortable then.'

He was frowning slightly, as if at some thought of

his own. His expression, though unfathomable, made Linda suspect that there was more to this invitation than the mere one of her conveniently making a fourth for dinner.

'Yes, but we were alone,' she reminded him.

'As I have assured you just now,' he said smoothly, 'you will like my friends, and they, I am sure, will be pleased to meet you.'

He added that Leonor would tell her where to find the best boutique and then without affording her the chance of further protestation he swung away and strode with his customary fluid grace and dignity towards the door of his study.

Linda wondered, as she put on the ankle-length evening dress, just what the Conde would think when he received the bill. Just how she had succumbed to the temptation to buy this particular dress she could not explain, for she had known its price was above what her employer would expect to pay. But immediately on seeing it, brought from somewhere at the back of the shop by the tall, dignified Frenchwoman whose boutique it was, Linda had had eyes for nothing else. And once it was on . . .

'It *is* madam!' was the simple yet eloquent verdict of the woman as she stood back so that Linda could take a full view of herself in the mirror. Of Edwardian style, with ruffles of pure silk lace at the throat and wrists, it seemed to disguise any defects in Linda's appearance. The cut was such that her thinness was not apparent, the full, gathered skirt having a semi-stiff petticoat beneath it. The waist was nipped in; the bodice seemed to cling despite the lost weight of its wearer's breasts. Only the length was wrong, for Linda was of average height and the dress had been designed for someone a little taller.

'The colour is exquisite for your hair,' the woman declared. 'Delicate green—orchid green it is called because it is the exact colour of a rare orchid that grows in the Far East. You will not see another of this colour, or of this style,' the woman assured her. 'Shall I bring in the needlewoman to pin up the hem for you?'

If Linda had had any doubts left by this time the woman's words erased the last of them. Linda could not have brought herself to say she was not having the dress, and then had to trouble the woman by asking to see others.

And now that it was on she began to wonder if she ought to have gone in for something with a little less material about it. A low-cut, sleeveless gown. . . . But no; it would have brought out all the thinness, the bones. Besides, this colour, and especially now that she had used the blusher and lip-rouge, flattered her, and the sallowness was no longer apparent. In any case, she was in fact losing her sallowness. Since coming here she had been eating well, taking her breakfast and lunch with the children in the Nursery Suite, and her dinner in the evening in her room. At home she had often picked at her food but now, with the three children looking on, she had felt it incumbent on her to eat a good meal, if only to preclude the possibility of the children's picking at their food which, like all children at times, they were very likely to do.

She stood a long while before the mirror, and into her thought stream came David, who now and then—when they could afford the luxury of a baby sitter—would take her out to dine, usually on her birthday or a wedding anniversary. He had always been critical of what she wore and how she looked; and now, as she stood there, having dressed for the satisfaction of another man, she knew a strange and paradoxical warmth that her late husband would have heartily approved of her appearance at this moment. Her hair shone as it used to; her eyes were as bright as could be expected, and her lips were rosy, albeit with aid, but attractive nevertheless.

She wore a plain gold chain with a small amethyst and pearl pendant, a gift from her aunt in a moment of deep, deep concern after Linda had been weeping continuously for two whole days.

Linda loved the gift, would treasure it always because of the thought, the concern, that had led to the buying of it. Auntie Sal, she suspected, had gone without a few things in order to buy it.

As the moment approached when Linda knew she must go down she felt her heart fluttering, her nerves playing her up.

However, it had to be done, and with a sort of stoic resignation she went down the impressive, balustraded staircase, and proceeded to the saloon where, to her intense relief, Dom Duarte was alone. He was sitting but rose on her entry, his dark unfathomable gaze resting on her face after their brief and yet all-enveloping examination of her body. The smile came slowly, and she wondered if it really meant anything, or was it merely a gesture absently made?

'So this is the dress you chose.' He let his eyes sweep over her again and she felt she was being stripped. 'I congratulate you on your good taste . . . Linda.'

'Linda?' The repetition came swiftly, accompanied by a heightening of her colour.

'I feel the time has come for me to use your given name,' was the Conde's cool rejoinder.

'Oh . . . d-do you, Dom Duarte?' She was by the door, standing as if waiting for a call to go on stage! Trouble was her legs felt like jelly! She very much liked the way he spoke her name, with that accent which to her was foreign. The name seemed to roll off his tongue in almost gentle tones.

'You're embarrassed,' he declared unexpectedly. 'Do sit down, Linda, and let me get you a drink. Martini as before?' One eyebrow was raised; it gave him a most attractive look, as did the slight uplift of his mouth at one corner . . . the trace of a smile.

'Yes, please.' She watched the majestic sway of his lean lithe body as he went to the cabinet. 'Er—the others—your friends—haven't arrived yet?' She felt foolish as soon as the unnecessary question was phrased, but she knew she had to say something. It was strange, she mused, that whenever there was a lull between people in a room, someone had to break the silence and, having done so, felt embarrassed, aware that the words were merely inane for the most part.

Linda accepted the drink, her eyes never leaving him as he took his own drink and sat down.

'They'll be here directly,' was all he said in response to her words. 'How are you getting along with the children?' he then inquired. 'I saw you all playing ball on the lawn this afternoon. I take it they had done all their lessons?'

'Yes. And they were so good all morning that I wanted to give them a break—I mean, reward them. It was lovely out there on the lawn.' She stopped rather abruptly and her companion said softly,

'You used to play with your children like that?'

How understanding he was!

Linda nodded her head, unaware of the way her hair caught the light from the candles, or how healthy it was now looking after the way it used to be—the way it was when she first arrived here, at the Palacio de Dominga.

'We all used to play ball on the lawn—after the twins were a bit older, that was,' she added. 'They were only three and a bit when—when—'

'Ah, here are my friends,' broke in Dom Duarte, rising from his chair as the door opened and the couple were shown in by Vitor, immaculate in pin-striped trousers and a snow white linen jacket with white shirt and a black bow tie.

'Duarte!' The Portuguese girl was all smiles, her rather chubby face soon lifted to look into the Conde's eyes. Intently watching, and interested, Linda was at the same time puzzled at the lack of any deep affection as Dom Duarte touched the girl's cheek with his lips. He held out a hand to her brother and immediately made the introductions.

'Happy to meet you,' smiled Dona Lucia. 'You look very nice in that dress.'

'Thank you,' murmured Linda who was left in no doubt as to the sincerity of the comment. She heard Dom Duarte say,

'Lucia always makes a point of passing appreciative remarks if she likes someone, or what they are wearing.' Amusement edged his tone and was reflected in his eyes. This was one facet of his character that Linda had not seen before. Felipe was extending a hand; his grip was firm about her fingers. Linda managed a smile and said quietly,

'I'm happy to meet you—er . . . ?' She glanced at her employer for guidance but it was Felipe who spoke.

'Just call me Felipe. I have no title like my friend here.'

Linda did not think she could call him by his Christian name but she naturally refrained from saying so. Felipe was almost as tall as the Conde, but his features were fair, his hair a sort of straw colour, while that of Lucia was more golden and silky. She had blue-grey eyes—most attractive, thought Linda as her own eyes wandered from the girl to the man whom everyone expected her to marry. They were suited, decided Linda, both carrying that air of nobility and self-assurance. Lucia was dressed in a deep blue evening gown of taffeta, its stiffness sending the skirt out in the most attractive way. The neck was high, the sleeves short. Linda felt much better about her own dress for she had convinced herself that the other girl would be in a low-cut creation, revealing, and eye-catching to any male.

'Drinks?' Dom Duarte was at the cabinet, already pouring a brandy and this was for Felipe. Lucia was drinking the same as Linda. The four sat down, Linda opposite to Felipe, whose eyes upon her seemed rather puzzled now and then. Perhaps he was wondering how a mere nanny had been able to afford the kind of gown she was wearing.

'How are you liking our country?' Lucia put the question; she was leaning forward in her chair, hands clasped on her knees. She seemed disproportionately interested in Linda's reply.

'I like it very much.'

'That's a good thing.' Fleetingly she glanced at Dom Duarte and inexplicably Linda's nerves tingled.

'You might stay on, then, to look after Marianna's children?' Although it was a very natural question, a follow-up to what had been said, Linda had the strange conviction that—because he had asked it—he was in total ignorance of something that was going on between his sister and Dom Duarte. For at his words Lucia's eyes sped instantly to the Conde's and their eyes locked for a fleeting and unfathomable moment before the Conde said smoothly,

'We're here to enjoy our evening, so let us leave business matters until another time.'

As the evening progressed Linda found herself more and more puzzled by the attitude of Lucia and Dom Duarte towards each other. She was remembering the phone call earlier when her aunt had said that Mrs. Sutherland had had it on good authority that an engagement was to be expected very soon.

Well, decided Linda by the time the meal was over and they were drinking their coffee in the lounge part of the room, if there was to be a marriage between the two it certainly wasn't based on love. Good friends, yes, with a certain enviable camaraderie, but affection . . . ? Not a hint of it in evidence.

By the time the couple were leaving Linda's mind had captured another impression, one that left her more bewildered than ever. She could not rid herself of the conviction that Dom Duarte had invited the couple to dinner for the specific purpose of showing his new employee to the girl!

And this naturally resulted in the recall of another impression, one she had at the time the Conde was asking her to join his party. His expression had been a mask but something about it had caused her to form the conclusion that there was much more to the invitation than that of her making up the even number, the fourth at dinner.

# Chapter Five

It was three weeks later and Linda was beginning to marvel at the change in herself and her outlook towards life. She had explored the Palacio, discovering one miracle of beauty after another, discovering also that there were two very different styles of architecture in the Palacio, one much older than the other. This was a sort of castle and she discovered that it was not in use and had not been for some considerable time. The main part was of Moorish design, with patios and arches, elaborate columns of alabaster or dark silver-grey marble. Apart from the sweeping staircase she had first ascended, there were two others, leading to wide carpeted corridors off which were massive rooms and suites luxuriously fitted up with antiques, priceless carpets and exquisite drapes. Outside there were more surprises in the sunken rose gardens, the lily ponds over-hung with dainty willows, the waterfall which formed a delightful feature of the Japanese garden. And away among the 'wild' part of the extensive grounds was a Grecian temple built on the lines of the exquisite Temple of Nike which stood on the Acropolis of Athens. The children loved to play in it, also in and around the only folly, the replica of a Norman castle along with a church and even the graveyard, this latter's headstones all small and beautiful, and bearing the names, mainly, of dogs, but one or two other pets' names were to be seen. 'Billy the goat,' 'Daisy the pony' and 'Brownie the hamster.' All long dead, as were their owners, owners who had grown up here from birth, had grown old and were buried in the churchyard down in the little town of Monvais—or, rather, just on the outskirts, where the church was situated, by the river.

Linda had wandered for hours in these gardens, mainly after the children had been put to bed, for their uncle insisted they go no later than half past seven. It was too early, thought Linda, though she was often tired by that time and ready to welcome the relaxation of the garden where cool breezes fanned her face and delightful perfumes assailed her receptive nostrils. She had grown to love the children, all so different but, as she had asserted at the very beginning, all most attractive in their own particular ways. In the morning Clara would greet her boisterously, most likely with the words, 'Oh, but I'm hungry!'

Felix would enter the breakfast room of the Nursery Suite far more sedately, that fine-boned

face serious, and yet always there followed a smile
as he greeted the girl who, for some reason of their
own, they had decided to call Auntie Linda. Vasco,
so tall for his age, would enter with the fine fluid
grace of his uncle, and sometimes Linda would find
herself, as she studied him intently, thinking it was
a pity he wasn't Dom Duarte's son, and the heir to
all this wealth and grandeur. As it was, he would be
fairly well-off, though. Dom Duarte had said that
his sister, once disinherited, would probably now
be able to claim something of what she had been
deprived. Leonor, in one of her moments of confid-
ing, had said that the Conde would be sure to give
her a share of his wealth anyway, even if she failed
to do anything about the vast sum which her father,
disgusted by her marriage, had left in trust for a
nephew who had since died.

Three weeks. . . . Linda marvelled once again,
as she strolled by the heated, illuminated
swimming-pool with its wide patio and masses of
flowering plants set in decorative pots all around it,
at the change in herself. Everyone had been right
when they said she ought to try to forget. She had
made the resolve and determinedly kept to it,
helped enormously by the fact that she was kept
busy for the whole of the day. Brooding in her
aunt's small house had been bad; she saw that now.
She ought to have gone back to work—could, she
knew, have been taken on by Mr. Fielding, who had
always said, when she happened to bump into him
after her marriage, that he would never have a
secretary quite as efficient as she. There had been a

vacancy three months after the accident and, see-ing the advertisement in the newspaper, Auntie Sal had tentatively suggested that Linda go and see if she could obtain the post. But, aided by the fact of her having a pension, plus a small sum from her late husband's firm, Linda had not made any effort to reshape her life.

Now, though, she was feeling altogether differ-ent. Not that the pain had lessened very much, but certainly it had done so a bit.

'I was right,' stated the Conde one day when he came upon her in the garden. 'The fact of your being occupied is helping you to forget.' Something of a curious nature ran as an undercurrent through these words, but Linda could not put her finger on it. All she knew was that she had the impression that the Conde was waiting for something. . . . For her to improve even more? Why, though? It was all too baffling and she wasted no more time on it.

She was staring into the pool when she swung around on hearing footsteps.

'Dom Duarte. . . .' She was all confusion with-out knowing why.

'I thought I might find you here.' He seemed to her nervous imagination to be all aloof detach-ment; she feared he might be here to admonish her because that afternoon Clara had given cheek to Adolfo, the handyman about the house who also did such jobs as looking after the pool and sweep-ing paths.

Clara had wanted to go in for a swim after lessons but as Adolfo was vacuuming it he told her she must wait. That was when Clara gave him cheek in plenty, much to Linda's horror. She had made Clara go inside but as she turned away she heard Adolfo mumble something in his own language and when she asked Clara what it was the child said that Adolfo was going to tell her uncle what she had done.

'But I don't care,' declared Clara with bravado. 'He's stupid so why can't I tell him he is?'

'Because it's very rude!'

Clara was unrepentant and so Linda refused to allow her out again. Now, she waited, her heart thudding with unnatural force against her ribcage.

'You—wanted to—to say something to me?' she managed at length.

'Yes. I would like to take you out on Thursday, Linda. My sister's giving a dinner party and of course I'm invited. I have told her you'll be coming with me.'

Staggered by this pronouncement Linda could only stare blankly at him. But she was recalling so many things that had happened lately, not least of which was that the Conde had asked her to dine with him no less than four times during the past two weeks. He had given her several lifts into the town, saying one of the maids would see to the children while she was away. It was plain that he wished her to buy some clothes and equally plain that he knew she would not accept any more from him. So he had paid her month's salary before it was due. She had told him that her aunt was sending on her clothes, and some books and other possessions, but still she was convinced that she was expected to buy clothes from one or other of the exclusive boutiques in town. She had bought a silk suit and some tight-fitting jeans, some shoes and a handbag, amazed at the pleasure these purchases were giving her when for so long she had been content with nothing new.

'I don't really want to go with you,' she began then bit her lip in embarrassment at her lack of tact. 'What I mean is . . .' She tailed off, aware that he was going to interrupt.

'Another order, I'm afraid,' he said. From under dark brows his eyes moved over her. 'I think the dress you bought at first will do,' he added presently.

She passed her tongue over lips that had gone dry. She was remembering something she had inadvertently overheard when Dom Duarte was using the telephone in the hall. Linda had been at the far end, watering some plants.

'So you are quite happy about it, Lucia?'

And, a moment later,

'It will solve all the problems, yours, Lucia, and mine. But of course her grief is still very much with her. . . .' Linda had moved away and she heard no more, but she felt sure that the Conde was referring to her when he mentioned grief. Just why that should come to her now Linda could not have explained, not any more than the tingling of nerve-ends and the sudden tenseness affecting her stomach muscles.

'I really must go with you, then?' she heard

herself say at length, and she lifted her eyes to his, appealing eyes and wide. There was a thread of understanding and compassion. It was strange, she mused, that he could be so dignified, so aristocratic and often unapproachable, and yet so kind.

'You'll enjoy it,' he assured her gently. 'You'll like my sister, Inez—and as it'll be late-ish her children won't be about.'

This last bit drew Linda's mind from the concern she felt about having to attend Inez's dinner party.

'You don't think I would want to see her children?'

'They're—brats, I believe you call really naughty children in your country.' He stopped and she half expected to see a thread of amusement on his eyes but instead they were frowning. She recalled the sudden change of manner in Leonor when she mentioned Inez's children. They would be here at Christmas and Linda couldn't help wondering how Clara would get on with them—Clara with her almost belligerent attitude if something happened to displease her. She was unpredictable, this Linda had discovered, though she still liked the child, very much. Her own two had even at three years of age shown spirit and Linda felt it only right that children should have spirit, have their own personalities and, in most cases, to be allowed to develop them normally.

'I suppose, basically, they are nice enough,' she found herself saying.

'Because you appear to like all children,' he said. 'But, believe me, these two are not at all like

Marianna's three.' That was all; Linda became uncomfortable in the ensuing silence and as if aware of it the Conde suggested they go inside and have a drink. She whispered to herself as she fell into step beside him,

'I wish I could understand you, Dom Duarte.'

They walked slowly, and the moon above was full, shedding its argent light over the lovely grounds and the valley where the vineyards were—lush grapes flourishing on the terraces. Linda found herself looking forward to the vintage—then pulled herself up with the reminder that she hadn't yet fully made up her mind to stay on in Portugal permanently. The Conde was speaking, saying that the following week-end he would be flying over to England to see his sister in hospital.

'Perhaps you would like to come with me?' he suggested and so staggered was she that she stopped dead in her tracks and stared disbelievingly up at him.

'I am employed to look after the children,' she began.

'Tereza will take care of them, or one of the others. They won't mind for a couple of days. I thought you might like to see your aunt.'

'I'd love to, but—'

'It's settled, then.' And that was that. Linda refused to form mental pictures of her and the august Conde Duarte Alfonso Laurenco de Dominga travelling together on an airplane!

Dom Duarte was walking on again.

'I'd like to meet your aunt,' he said calmly.

81

'You . . . !' Again her legs refused to carry her forward. 'Oh, but we live in a very small house and—and . . .'

'I expect you do.' His tone was still coolly unconcerned. 'Something like that of Mrs. Sutherland, perhaps?'

She stared up at him.

'Yes, that's right.'

'I've been there—a few weeks ago when my sister first became ill.'

'You've visited Mrs. Sutherland's house?' If he noticed her amazed expression he chose to ignore it completely.

'Why not? She was willing to take the children and at that time we hadn't realised that my sister was quite so seriously ill. We supposed she would be out of hospital in a week or so.'

Linda moved on, skipping now to keep up with her companion's rather swift pace. She felt dwarfed beside him . . . and strangely happy, light of heart . . . a new experience and it was so very nice.

'Mrs. Sutherland didn't say you'd visited her.'

'No? But she is one of those reticent people who tell only what is necessary. I gather she told you very little about either my sister, Marianna, or myself . . . nothing about our private lives, for instance?'

'No, nothing.' Why had he hesitated, she wondered. She was walking very close to him because they were now traversing a very narrow pathway between borders of flowering shrubs. She felt his nearness, caught the heady smell of body talc which mingled with the pervasive male smell of him.

The fine hairs on Linda's arms lifted, for no reason at all. Her body was light when she and the Conde began to walk more briskly again.

She tried to drag her mind from the wonder of it all, from the sensation of pleasure, and to think of David and her two lost children . . . but it was impossible. Tears filled her eyes and she did not know why. Looking sideways at her Dom Duarte said,

'You look tired. We must have that drink and then I'm going to order you to bed.'

She coloured up, unaware of the beauty created or the unwanted interest of the man at her side. There was a curious, unfathomable expression on his handsome face but to Linda it went unnoticed. Emotions within her were aroused . . . new emotions she had never known before. What was happening to her? This man was altogether too attractive; his magnetism was too powerful by far. She wanted only to live with her memories . . . or had done so when first she came here, to this palatial home, this patrician among the other *quintas* of this region of Portugal . . . the fascinating Douro Valley.

She lifted her face, and all at once magic was in the air. Without a word Dom Duarte bent his dark head and kissed her full on the lips.

And then he was walking swiftly again, as if he were angered by what he had done.

With colour radiant in her cheeks, she was

presently in the Blue Drawing Room of the Palacio, the smallest of the sitting-rooms and the one used most. Tumbled cushions; and letters that were tucked behind ornaments on the white marble mantelpiece; a rug made by hand, yet exquisite in its design. Linda loved the Blue Drawing Room, perhaps because it was not as grand as its name implied. Incongruous and snug, appealing and warm, welcoming and as cosy as any nest.

Dom Duarte gave her a drink and poured a brandy for himself. He came and stood over her. And it was only in that moment of near intimacy that she saw why he had arranged—oh, yes, it had been arranged!—to take her out, where she would be with others and forget that it was the anniversary of the accident.

Linda knew a full flood of warmth and well-being, a surge of deep affection for the man who seemed to have set himself the task of her salvation.

A lovely smile transformed her features and his eyes widened strangely. He said, right out of the blue,

'Will you marry me, Linda?'

The room spun; she gripped the arms of the chair, her mouth open, her eyes wide and staring.

She swallowed at last.

'I'm dreaming,' she said, but silently. The Conde, his eyes moving fractionally to her right hand whose knuckles were bleached, so tightly were her fingers clenched, repeated his question in a smooth unemotional voice, his eyes returning to

her face. It was white and her mouth now moved
convulsively.

'You must be mad,' she heard herself say in a
cracked little tone.

The hint of a smile brought amusement flickering
in his fine dark eyes. She stared up at him, as he
stood there, close to her chair. There was a dynam-
ic quality about him which had no relationship with
his exalted status as the Conde de Dominga, an
aura of forcefulness despite the calm and casual
pose he was adopting on the surface. Linda shook
her head as if to clear it of a mist of incomprehen-
sion.

'I—you . . .' Her voice failed her; she still felt
she was dreaming. 'You s-said we'd have a dr-
drink, if you remember. . . .'

The smile deepened. Yet in his eyes there was a
sort of pity mingled with understanding.

'You're thinking of your husband, and probably
of the vow you made yourself that no one would
ever take his place?'

She nodded dumbly. This insight seemed to
bring some kind of sanity to the situation for it was
now clear in her mind that this illustrious nobleman
*had* asked her to marry him.

She leant back in the chair and closed her eyes.

'You feel you need that drink.' His voice was
edged with humour; she heard him go over to the
cabinet, heard the drink being poured into a glass.

She opened her eyes.

'I can't marry you,' she said in a daze. 'I think
you are mad, or dr—' She pulled herself up.

'I assure you I am neither mad nor drunk,' was his immediate denial; she marvelled that he was not furious at her words. Perhaps he understood that she did not know what to say, or how to deal with this fantastic situation in which she found herself. 'I hadn't intended asking you just yet,' he added. 'Still, no harm is done.'

He was handing her the drink and she came forward in the chair. How could he be so calm!

She said what was in her mind.

'There've been things I haven't understood right from the beginning—well, almost from the beginning.' He was still above her; her eyes clung to his pleadingly. 'You'll explain?' she beseeched and after the merest pause he nodded his head.

'Eight years ago I was engaged to a lovely Portuguese girl. . . .' For a few seconds he was drifting away from her. 'It was a love match. . . .' Again a pause. Linda's eyes flickered; she was remembering that when she had said her husband was twenty-two when they were married, Dom Duarte had murmured to himself. He'd been remembering his own love affair. 'She died while swimming in the sea; she had a cramp and there was no one near.' He stopped, emotion taking him into the past again. 'Like you, Linda, I felt life held nothing; I drifted for a while, wanting to die, to go to her. But time does heal to some extent. With you, two years only have gone by; with the passing of another few years you too will find that life does in fact hold something, that happiness is still to be found— No, don't shake your head, Linda, for already, since you came here only a month ago, I have seen a change in you. Admit it,' he added and she nodded then and said yes, he spoke the truth.

'It's the fact that I'm fully occupied,' she added, just for something to say.

Calmly Dom Duarte proceeded,

'I think you will appreciate that a man in my position must marry and have children—'

'Dona Lucia,' she broke in, feeling hysterical as the whole picture of what the Conde had in mind unfolded itself to her. 'You are almost engaged to her. Mrs. Sutherland said so. And why didn't Mrs. Sutherland mention this tragedy in your life . . . ?' Linda pulled herself up abruptly, aware that this question had no relevance at all.

'She doesn't gossip. We've already mentioned this I believe.'

'Yes.'

'To get back to what I was saying: I ought to marry. Dona Lucia and I are not in love—but you must have noticed this?'

'Yes,' said Linda briefly again.

'In some of our families here marriages are— shall we say—hoped for rather than arranged. There was a time when I half agreed with Lucia's parents that a match between us would be looked upon favourably by me, and as Lucia has been brought up to observe strict obedience to her parents she initially fell in with their wishes.'

'They wanted their daughter to marry you, knowing you weren't in love with her?'

'Often the material aspect is more important than love. It was to be like this in the case of Lucia and me. However, as time went on Lucia made it more and more plain that she wanted to marry for love and the problem then was: how could we manoeuvre the situation so as not to reveal to her parents that it was Lucia who wanted to back out of the agreement.'

'It was an agreement rather than an engagement, then?'

He inclined his head.

'At that time, yes. The engagement would be announced only when we were prepared to fix the date for the wedding.' He paused, then went on, his tone quite casual, 'Marriages can succeed without love—in certain circumstances. But between Lucia and me it would never have worked and we both realised it—after a time, that was, for at first Lucia was younger and reluctant to do anything of which her parents would disapprove.'

'So you want it to appear that it is your fault that the arrangements have fallen through? That you are—well—letting Lucia down?'

He nodded at once.

'That is correct,' he said.

'But—' Linda spread her hands. 'There are dozens of women who would be willing to marry you. . . .' Her voice trailed at his expression which was one of amusement.

'You are very flattering,' was his smooth rejoinder.

She wasn't put out, which surprised her.

'It's true and you must know it, Dom Duarte.'

He politely agreed but went on to say,

'What can I give to a woman in return for what I want from her?'

'You might fall in love one day.'

'It's unlikely. As with you, Linda, I live with a wonderful memory.'

'But you said you'd recovered.'

'From the pain, yes, and so will you do so, as I've said. But the memory is with me, the happy times we shared, the love.' He looked significantly at her and she found herself saying,

'You think a marriage between you and me would succeed because neither of us will expect anything from the other?'

'There will be many things we can give . . . but not love.'

She fell silent, conscious of a weight within her, and the sigh in her heart was beyond comprehension. Her mind was confused by the subconscious awareness that she was considering his proposal.

'You are thinking that, with me, there is no possibility of my wanting love from you?' She paused but he said nothing. He seemed to have drifted from her and she knew he was with his lost love. 'With another woman—well—she might one day fall in love with you and, as you couldn't give her love in return it would be disastrous for you both.'

'You have the picture.' The Conde's voice was smooth and casual.

Linda was slowly shaking her head from side to side.

'I can't marry you,' she murmured and wondered why there was no supporting conviction in her mind.

'You haven't given the matter any consideration,' he reminded her. He walked over to a chair and lowered himself into it. 'If you accepted you'd have children of your own again— No, they'd never take the place of the others,' he added when she was about to interrupt. 'But you'd love them; they'd give *you* love.' He looked gravely at her. 'You might not believe it at this moment but they *would* compensate.'

She clamped her teeth together. Deep within her she was admitting that he had a point. With his uncanny perception he knew that the void within her needed to be filled, that although she would never love another man she could in fact love her children just as deeply as she had loved the first two. She thought of Marianna's children and how in a short time she had become deeply attached to them.

'I can't marry you,' she said again in a weak little voice.

He ignored that as he went on to explain that he had let her meet Lucia so that Lucia could— casually in passing—mention to her parents that a young Englishwoman had come to work for him and that it seemed to Lucia that he was quickly becoming attracted to her.

'So you've already began to—to pave the way!' gasped Linda. Lucia was to work on her parents, it seemed. This was what was being discussed between Dom Duarte and Lucia when Linda heard him on the telephone.

'If you care to put it that way,' was Dom Duarte's cool reply.

'But you weren't sure of my answer!'

'I rather felt that once you had given the matter some thought you would find my offer attractive. After all, your aunt is old and might not be able to have you with her—if you decided to return, that is. You have your future to consider,' he went on seriously. 'If you marry me all your financial worries would be solved—'

'I don't care about money!'

'But we all need it,' was the Conde's very practical response. 'You'll be old one day,' he reminded her and suddenly she was poised on a knife-edge of balance between what was the practical thing to do and her fervid resolve to remain totally true to David's memory. Yet already she was able at times to forget the past, to go for several hours freed from that dragging weight in the pit of her stomach.

And she had in all honesty to admit that life now was much more bearable than it had been before she came here, to Dom Duarte's home.

He was saying into her thoughts,

'I don't want your answer at this very moment. Sleep on it and we'll talk again in the morning.'

She nodded and he changed the subject after silently watching her sip her drink.

'I can meet your aunt when we go over at the week-end.'

Her eyes darted to his.

'It was because you hoped I'd marry you that you suggested a meeting with Auntie Sal, wasn't it?'

'Yes, it was.'

'And this dinner with your sister . . . it's on the—the anniversary of the accident.'

The Conde inclined his head.

'It will take your mind off things,' he said equably. 'I always found that the evenings were the worst, so we shall go out.' He smiled slowly. 'Don't be grateful,' he said. 'I'm wanting something from you, remember.'

'But you are kind just the same,' she just had to say.

'You are in need of kindness just now,' he observed with an understanding that edged through the veneer of matter-of-factness.

'I need—advice,' she murmured without knowing why she should be saying anything like that. For who could know what was best for her—who but herself? And as she was so bewildered that she could scarcely think, she welcomed his saying that it was time she was in bed.

She had finished her drink so she eased herself from the chair and straightened up.

'As for the advice you mention,' the Conde said as she reached the door which he was holding open for her, 'try to take mine. You'll not regret it if you marry me, I assure you of that.'

'I've said, several times, that I can't marry you.' She faltered, a cloud of tears gathering at the backs of her eyes.

'But your mind isn't by any means made up,' he asserted rather chidingly so that all at once she felt very young . . . and vulnerable. It was hard to believe he was less than four years older than she, adopting as he was this fatherly manner with her. She could find nothing to say to his perceptive statement and she saw the censure in his eyes fade out as the silence stretched. 'You'll decide to marry me,' he said with conviction at last and she stared expressionlessly back at him, aware of odd, feathery ripples along her spine as her senses took in everything about him—the handsome, Latin-type features, the splendour of his physique with not an ounce of excess weight on his muscled frame. What was this new and almost exhilarating sensation for which he alone was responsible? The attractive male odour of him assailed her nostrils as he moved a little, as if he would remind her that he was waiting for her to go.

'I'll think well about what you've said,' she promised, speaking rather slowly because she suddenly had an urge to stay for a while. And yet . . . paradoxically, she wanted the sanctuary of her bedroom where she could make some attempt to collect her scattered thoughts and come to a firm decision from which she would not waver.

# Chapter Six

Linda stood watching Dom Duarte playing with the three children and stirrings unfathomable affected her heart and her mind. It wasn't as if she were seeing her husband with her own children.

No, he had begun to fade during these last weeks and, strangely, Linda had no feeling of guilt. She would never forget him, as Dom Duarte had so wisely told her, but she would find she could think of the happy days, when they were a happy family and there was no pain.

'Don't throw the ball so hard . . . !' cried Clara. Her voice faded as Adolfo, having been swinging along carrying a basket of vegetables he had picked for the evening meal, stooped and picked up the ball which had landed at his feet. 'Just you give that to me—' The child went off into Portuguese but within seconds she had uttered a cry of pain and protest after a slap from her uncle had brought the impudent words to an abrupt stop.

'Apologise to Adolfo,' ordered Dom Duarte sternly and without hesitation Clara muttered something in Portuguese, then turned away.

'She's getting too cheeky,' in English from Vasco. 'It was that school we went to in England. She was always fighting the other children—'

'There is no need for tale-carrying,' put in his uncle. And then, 'Off you all go. We'll play again another day.'

'But—oh, it's all her fault . . . !'

'That's enough, Vasco; no arguments please.'

The children went off but when Linda made to accompany them her employer said,

'Go to Tereza and ask her to give you your tea. Auntie Linda and I want to talk.'

When they had gone he drew nearer to where she was standing, her hair, gleaming now with health, a little tousled by the breeze. She lifted a hand to it, conscious of her thin, voile-like dress being affected by the breeze too, shaping itself to her curves. Dom Duarte's eyes wandered from her face to her figure and she could not help but notice the expression in their depths . . . an expression that served to remind her that, if she married him, it most certainly would not be one of convenience in that it would not be normal. Of course, he had said he wanted an heir—a family. But somehow at that time Linda had gained the impression that the consummation of the marriage might not take place for some time. But now . . .

She recalled an earlier impression that the

Conde was a particularly virile man and now she knew for sure that there would be no delay once the wedding day came to its close, no period of adjustment. Dom Duarte was marrying her because he had reached that point in his life when the single state no longer satisfied him.

'You want to talk to me?' She felt immeasurably shy and inadequate even while she again knew that feeling of exhilaration she had experienced last night.

'Yes; I'm thinking of sending the three children to school rather than have you give them lessons.' He was beside her; she felt the power of him, the draw of his personality. Tingles of pleasure seemed irrational for surely only love made you feel like this?

'But I shan't have anything to do,' she heard herself protest. 'Not if they're out all day.'

'You'll have plenty to do.' He took her arm and led her over to a rustic seat tucked away in a little arbour where the scent of roses pervaded the air and other miracles of beauty abounded—the oleanders with their wax-like flowers of pink and white, the magnolias so creamy-pink and elegant, the sunlight on the acacias adding more gold to their colouring. Overhead the sky was a clear azure blue and from the low hills the breeze came sweeping down to stir the lovely Travellers palms that grew in lush perfection along one side of the formal gardens. A fountain played, its spray taking sun colours to create a rainbow effect. A peacock flaunting its finery, a few brightly-coloured smaller birds, too, and the marble cupids coyly staring down on it all from their Corinthian-style pedestals. 'I had a conversation with my sister on the phone earlier today. She is quite cheerful, and I suppose that is because she does know she will be cured eventually. She expressed the wish that the children be settled in school as soon as possible because she has decided to accept a house not too far from here which I own.' He turned his dark head to look at the girl he had asked to be his wife. 'Marianna can't possibly go into that house in its present state, Linda. I have never contemplated having a tenant in it because it is actually on the estate, although on the border. I haven't done anything to it since I took over this estate from my father; He had not done anything either. It was once the home of my widowed grandmother—Father's mother—and since her death it has been unoccupied.' He paused and Linda wondered why he was going into so much detail like this. However, she was not to remain puzzled for long. 'I want you to take over and have it put right—'

'Me? But I—well, I wouldn't know how to begin! Not on a stately home like that.' She was thinking of the house she had lived in with her husband and children, a modest little home charmingly decorated and furnished in accordance with the combined tastes of its owners . . . but in comparison with what would be wanted in order to set a house to rights for Marianna. . . . 'I'd not make a success of it,' she added decisively.

To her surprise he smiled. Her nerve-ends quivered at the attractiveness of him and she glanced swiftly away, bewildered by her feelings.

Was it possible that she, like the Conde, had reached the point where the single life no longer satisfied her? She had been passionate in the reciprocation to her husband's love. . . .

She felt the blood rising in her cheeks, the result of embarrassment at her own thoughts, and it was at that particular moment that the Conde chose, for some reason, to turn her face round and compel her to look at him. The dark unfathomable eyes subjected her to a keen scrutiny and she would have turned from him again if it had been at all possible but his hold on her chin was firm and imperious.

'What are you thinking about to make you blush like that?' he inquired, just as she had expected he would.

'I—it—was nothing,' she murmured and although it seemed at first that he would question her again, he released her instead, much to her relief.

'To get back to this house—the Casa de Rialta it's called. We shall go over first thing in the morning— No, Linda!' he said imperiously when she would have interrupted him. 'Kindly listen to me. Tereza will look after the children if that is what you are worrying about. As I said, you and I will go over to take a look over the Casa and make an assessment about any structural alterations that it might require.' He paused a moment in thought. 'I don't think there are any major changes necessary—'

'Dom Duarte,' broke in Linda risking a censure, 'the responsibility would be too much for me.

Supposing I did it as I would like it and then your sister doesn't care for my taste?'

'I have confidence in your taste,' said the Conde with that sort of inflection of finality that forbade any further argument. Linda coloured again but maintained a silence as he went on, 'I shall help you, of course, but in the main you'll be given a free hand.' He smiled and her pulses did strange things. 'I'm very sure that Marianna will be happy with the result of your endeavours.'

Linda was silent, her brow creased anxiously, for on the one hand she was highly flattered by his confidence in her ability to carry out the task successfully; on the other hand she really was troubled by the magnitude of the assignment.

Dom Duarte seemed deep in thought when presently she turned to look at him in profile. It was a nice silence that had come between them, she thought, a companionable one, totally without strain on her part. She leant back to enjoy the sun on her face as it filtered through the leaves of a jacaranda tree. She could just discern a gaily-plumaged bird preening its feathers on the bright green lawn, could appreciate the glowing colours of the gardens—lilies and petunias, tall cinerarias moving gently in the breeze so that their blue and white flowers seemed to reflect light and shade in the most attractive way.

At last the Conde broke the silence, rising as he did so.

'I must leave you, Linda, but we shall see each other at dinner time.' He left her. He was all charm and persuasion, she mused. The innate arrogance was there, of course, because it was part of him and always would be. But with her he had unbent; his smile was so pleasing to her that she actually felt happy every time she saw it. Happy. . . . A word she had not even thought of for so long. She had convinced herself that her life was owed to the memory of her husband and children and that it would be something in the nature of disloyalty if she even tried to be happy. Her aunt had always tried to instil into her that she had been given a life of her own and, therefore, she owed it to no one. But Linda had never been able to agree. Now, though, into the dark abyss of her memories had come this ray of light, this opportunity of living again and being able to feel. She was offered the chance of having children who would bring love into her heart once again.

She followed the tall distinguished figure with her eyes until it had gone from sight. Such a man to want her! A man of the Portuguese nobility who lived in his ancestral Palacio and who owned the vast Quinta de Dominga and so much more besides.

It was no wonder that she sometimes felt she must pinch herself just to make sure she was awake!

Immediately after breakfast the following morning Dom Duarte said they would go over to the Casa. He drove over in a small, two-seater car with the roof open, so that they were both a little wind-blown by the time Dom Duarte swung about on the wide semi-circular forecourt and came to a halt. Linda felt exhilarated and faintly breathless; she looked at the Conde and smiled, for he seemed so young—like a boy!—with his dark hair tousled like that, a rebellious little quiff falling on to his forehead after he had pushed it back and drawn his long lean fingers through it.

'Well,' he said, 'this is it.'

'It looks lovely.' The front was a pillared façade of mellowed, ochre-coloured stone with small towers at either end and patios which once had dripped with exotic flowers but which now were home for a tangle of vegetation which was a mixture of these once glorious plants and the invasion of weeds and gorse, this latter in bloom and giving a cheerful aspect to the otherwise faded glory of the past. There were several Moorish archways bordering a courtyard, this also overgrown with weeds. Linda noticed the delightful Italianate corner windows with their broad balconies set at right angles, the little rustic plaza with its vine-trellis matted against the south-facing wall, the superb situation of the property and its grounds, nestling as they did on the slope of one of the lesser sierras that screen the Valley of the Douro.

'You like it, then?' There was a hint of regret in the Conde's voice as he added without giving Linda time to reply, 'I feel I ought to have done something to it before now, and perhaps rented it to someone. But neither my father nor I really cared for the idea of anyone actually living on the estate.'

'It's a good distance from the Palacio, though.' Linda was standing by the car, staring up at the front façade again.

'It'll be just the thing for Marianna and the children. Come, I'll take you inside.'

'It's a bit like the Palacio only on a much smaller scale,' she was submitting half an hour later when they were outside again, in the sunshine. 'I love the curving staircase and the filigree decorations of some of the rooms. And the alabaster supports in the sitting-room—I suppose that one with the triple aspect will be the sitting-room?' she asked, pointing.

The Conde nodded his head.

'That's the one Marianna will use as the main living-room, I expect.'

'She's familiar with this place, obviously. But she hasn't seen it lately?'

He looked rueful, threaded fingers through his hair again to push back that unruly lock of hair.

'I don't think she's seen it since she left to live in England. When she and her family were here on holiday they were always occupied by more interesting things than visiting a—well—a ruin, almost.' He frowned as he spoke and Linda was swift to say,

'Oh, no, Dom Duarte! It's far from that! I shall make it really beautiful!' She pulled up rather abruptly, aware of what she had said even before her companion spoke.

'You are obviously more optimistic now you've seen the Casa?'

She nodded and smiled.

'It just invites interest,' she answered enthusiastically. But she just had to add, 'I do hope my ideas will be acceptable to Marianna.' It was the first time she had referred to his sister by her Christian name; it had come out accidentally and yet quite naturally. It struck her that if she did agree to marry the Conde then she would have a number of relatives, which would be nice because apart from her aunt, she had had no one since the accident.

'They will,' replied the Conde, bending to tug at a weed. She had to smile at the instinctive action; it made him even more human and she thought, not for the first time, that he was a man of very complex personality. A man born to inherit an ancient and honourable title along with a vast *quinta* and fortune and an army of employees.

'Shall we wander in the grounds?' he suggested. 'You'll find they're exceedingly overgrown but with a little imagination you can see what they used to be like many years ago—and what they can be like again.'

They wandered along side by side in companionable silence, with the warm air around them, moving the palms, causing tiny ripples on a lake where water lilies once had abounded.

Linda stared or glanced, taking in everything and thinking it a shame it had been so neglected. She wondered what the old, aristocratic lady who once resided here would think of her home if she could see it now. Yet Linda could understand the reluctance of the Conde to have anything done to it if he wasn't intending to have a tenant. It would have been illogical to keep it in immaculate order— for nothing.

But she was glad that it was now going to be lived in again; the children would bring brightness and laughter and warmth to it.

'The grounds are not going to present any difficulty,' she heard the Conde say as they stopped by the edge of the lake. 'My gardeners can spend some time here getting it all into shape; then we'll have the borders re-planted and the shrubbery filled in where bushes and trees have died.'

Money was no object, mused Linda and could not help recalling how she and her husband always had to save hard for everything they had—one thing at a time if it happened to be big. She remembered the lovely dry stone wall they had had built at the bottom of the garden; it had taken them over six months to save enough money for it.

On the way back Dom Duarte made a detour so that they could stop at a quaint little cafe for coffee. They sat outside beneath a canopy of vines through which darts of sunlight penetrated sufficiently to highlight Linda's hair, to give a glow to her eyes and to accentuate the high cheek bones with their clear, honey-toned skin stretched over them. No sallowness now and Linda did wonder, as she looked at herself in the mirror much later in the day, while she was dressing for dinner, what her aunt would have to say about the change in her appearance.

Dom Duarte certainly was satisfied, and he said so, again telling Linda that being fully occupied, and also the entire change of surroundings, and the interest she had in them, had worked a miracle in that she was beginning to forget—not her husband

and family, but the sadness of losing them. She agreed, drawn as she was by the Conde's compelling personality, and by his kindness and understanding.

That he could be stern, and even ruthless, she had no doubts. He had this very arrogant streak to his nature which would assert itself if circumstances should require the use of arrogance. He could be masterful, imperious and darkly forbidding. . . . Oh, yes, all these things as well as kindness compounded to form his very complex personality. He had seemed cold when first she met him, but now . . .

The way he was looking at her as she stood just inside the door of the dining saloon just before dinner. She was wearing a Dresden blue dress of shimmering pure silk, bought only a couple of days ago in town. Her blue-sandalled toes peeped from the hem of the full flared skirt. But it was higher up that the Conde's eyes were drawn to, where the bodice fit snugly as though caressing her breasts, and the waist was nipped in with a corded silver belt to match the cording on the high mandarin collar. Sleeveless, the dress was indeed a lovely creation for which Linda had paid over half her month's allowance.

'You look very lovely,' murmured Dom Duarte and, as if he just could not control the impulse, he stepped closer, tilted her head, and kissed her full on the lips.

'I feel sure you will marry me,' was his confident remark spoken over his shoulder as he moved to pull out a chair for her. Her own progress towards him was slow for she was still a little stunned by his action even though it was not the first time he had kissed her. She could feel the pressure of his mouth on hers. It seemed to have awakened every quivering nerve in her body; she felt excited, her heart pulsing so that she felt he must see the movement in her breast. She sat down and he took possession of the opposite chair. As usual the table was a sheer delight of luxury and exquisite taste, with flowers and candles to provide colour, crystal glass to glitter in the flickering lights, snow white table linen stiffly starched and smooth. Not a single flaw . . . which was only right for so exalted a person as the Conde.

He was watching her as her eyes moved over the table.

'It's all so—so beautiful,' she murmured for she knew he was waiting for some comment.

'It can be yours all the time, Linda,' he reminded her simply and she nodded and smiled and said with a sort of tremulous optimism,

'My decision isn't quite so hard now. . . .'

'You've become used to the idea, is that it?' His interest was revealed by the way he looked at her with a direct stare.

Linda nodded her head.

'Yes, I'm certainly becoming used to the idea.'

His smile was as charming as the foreign voice with its accent which had caught Linda's attention from the very first moment of meeting him.

'We shall do very well together,' he stated. 'Didn't I say so before?'

Again she nodded, looking away from the dark, smiling countenance and refusing to dwell on whether or not she would fit in here, at the Palacio, or whether she would be accepted by his family. She was conscious of an indescribable breathlessness, and she felt he must be aware of the way she felt because an enigmatic smile curved his lips.

It was a relief to Linda when Vitor entered to serve the *saumon d'Ecosse fumé*. Dom Duarte poured the wine himself—champagne—and she thought: He probably knew I'd accept his proposal tonight! And it had happened so naturally that she scarcely knew she *had* settled her future!

Auntie Sal was all excitement when, about an hour after Linda and her fiancé had arrived at the little house, she and her niece were at last alone for a few minutes, Duarte having gone to use the telephone in the hall.

'I couldn't believe my ears when you rang to say you were going to marry the Conde! Oh, my love, I wish you happy!'

'Thank you, Auntie.' Linda's face was pale but composed. 'I did say we weren't in love with one another. I told you the circumstances, and that Duarte, like me, has lost the one he loved and so can never love another woman.'

Auntie Sal was frowning now as she met the wide and limpid gaze of her niece.

'Time will tell, my dear, what can happen.'

Linda had to smile.

'You're thinking that we shall fall in love, eventually?'

'I'm an optimist, Linda,' returned her aunt seriously. 'If one isn't these days where would we all be?'

'Duarte and I have made a contract, Auntie, and there is no possibility of either of us ever falling in love with the other. . . .' Her voice trailed away to a strange unfathomable silence for she could not ignore the way she had felt about Duarte recently —even before the beautiful diamond ring was put on her finger, and which had made her aunt gasp over and over again. Duarte's kindness, his infinite understanding . . . and most of all, his powerful magnetism which seemed to draw her physically so that, once she was engaged, she found herself quite unable to blot out from her mind pictures of a most intimate nature, even though she tried very hard to do so.

She had to admit in the end that the physical part of life was important and that her new husband would be in no way abhorrent to her.

'You're looking forward to the marriage, though,' she heard her aunt say and she nodded at once.

'Very much.'

The old lady shot her a strange glance but made no further comment on that.

'Tell me about Duarte's family,' she invited eagerly and Linda gave her descriptions of Inez and her husband, Antonio, her brothers, Juan and Diaz.

'Duarte took me to dinner at the Casa de Rivera where I met them all.' Linda paused a moment in recollection. 'They all seemed to like me, and seemed glad that at last Duarte was intending to marry.'

'But they'd have supposed him to be marrying this other girl you told me about?'

'Lucia? Yes, but Duarte had explained everything before we went to visit them and so they didn't show any surprise.'

'Duarte had told them that he was marrying you?'

'On the phone, yes.'

'Preparing them,' mused Auntie Sal. "All the same, it must have come as a shock to them to learn that he was marrying—well—a young lady from England.'

'A commoner—is that what you were going to say?' Linda was making a wry face. 'I am, of course, but the circumstances of our marriage being what they are it doesn't matter. As I explained to you in the long letter I sent after phoning you, Duarte would never have married anyone who would expect love from him.'

'You're so calm about it!' protested the old lady, looking a trifle concerned now. 'It all sounds cold and clinical—'

'We do intend to have children, Auntie,' broke in Linda without even a hint of embarrassment, 'so it isn't really cold and clinical.'

A deep sigh escaped her aunt.

'I'm glad as you know, at the turn of events, love. But knowing you, and that warm loving nature—' She stopped and spread her hands. 'You might feel it's all right now, at this moment in time, but, with a man as attractive as the Conde—well, you are quite apt to fall in love one day, and fall heavily. Happy as I am that at last you have come out of yourself, I'm worried all the same, in case you're in for heartbreak a second time.'

Linda was silent a moment, musing again on the way she had begun to feel about the man who was soon to be her husband.

Was it possible that even now she was beginning to fall in love with him? She dismissed the idea simply because she had no wish to carry it further, to a time when, as her aunt had suggested, she might find herself wildly in love with Duarte.

'To look too far into the future is unprofitable,' she said logically at length. 'Fate holds our lives in its hands, Auntie, and there really isn't very much we can do about it.'

Auntie Sal looked at her.

'You always did maintain that our lives were mapped out even from the moment we were born.'

Linda nodded her head. Auntie Sal regarded her in the small silence that followed, marvelling yet again—as she had marvelled at the moment of seeing her niece again after the relatively short absence—at the dramatic change in her appearance. No sallowness to add ten years to her age, no neglect of hair and general appearance. She had appeared as a young girl, beautifully dressed and with hair shining, skin glowing with a delectable honey-tan picked up from the warmth and sun of Portugal. Her eyes were bright; her smile came easily.

'Our fate must be mapped out,' said Linda

presently. 'For otherwise these things would not happen to us.'

'You have said, several times, that you wished that you were in the car—'

'I know. Well, it was fate that I stayed at home.'

'And escaped . . . to find this magnificent man who, though seeming to be a little too proud, is charming. I like him, Linda, but all the same, I shall worry about your future.'

They were in the sitting-room and Linda rose swiftly from her chair by the window and, crossing over to her aunt, she bent and gave her a little hug and a kiss.

'You're not to worry about a thing,' she said trying to be stern. 'I feel perfectly satisfied with my decision—'

'Oh, I'd not have it otherwise,' interrupted her aunt swiftly. 'No one could be more delighted than I at what has transpired. You need a husband . . . but you need love and I rather feel that love might come to you both one day. Until then, pet, I shall be a little anxious, which, after all, is natural, isn't it?'

'I agree,' smiled her niece. But she made no comment on the rest of what her aunt had said. The future would take care of itself.

Duarte came back into the room and sat down. Auntie Sal looked at him with that all-examining stare she had directed at him at the moment of introduction by her niece. She had said he was rather too proud but she did concede that he had every right to be, seeing that he was of the nobility, that he was the owner of such a vast estate. A small sigh escaped her as she transferred her gaze to her niece.

'I ought to be satisfied with small mercies,' she breathed to herself. 'At least she's snapped out of her introverted mood and is fast recovering from that dreadful tragedy.'

Linda and her aunt accompanied Duarte when he went to visit Alice Sutherland; he had hired a car at the airport and so he drove them there, looking far too regal for the small, nondescript vehicle which was all the car-hire firm had to offer at such short notice.

Both Linda and her aunt were surprised at the easy way in which Alice could converse with the Conde. She had of course been told of the engagement by her friend, Linda's aunt, but although she warmly congratulated them and wished them happy, she evinced no surprise or emotion of any kind. Whatever her feelings and thoughts she kept them to herself.

'You're taking me with you to the hospital, of course,' she said as if this were taken for granted.

'Most certainly,' agreed that urbane foreign voice. 'Marianna will be equally as pleased to see you as she will be to see me.' He paused and glanced across at his fiancée. 'And she is very eager to meet you, Linda.'

Linda said nothing. She knew Duarte had written to his sister, as well as speaking with her by telephone.

'I expect you are looking forward to meeting your future sister-in-law.' Alice's expression remained unreadable. 'I believe Marianna's progress is rather better than was at first expected,' she added, speaking to the Conde.

'Yes; I spoke with one of her doctors on the telephone yesterday, just before we left home, and he was most reassuring.'

'The children will be happy to have her back.'

'Very happy.' Suddenly his mouth was tight and it was easy to see that his mind had flashed to the children's father. Linda had learned from Inez that, once she was home, Marianna would divorce her husband.

'You'll be wanting a nanny for them.'

Duarte nodded his head.

'That will be looked into at a later date, once we know my sister's coming home. Meanwhile—' He paused to smile at his fiancée. 'Linda will carry on, but with much help from Tereza.'

'I'll just go and get myself ready,' from Alice as she rose from her chair. 'The roads are busy in this part of town and it might take us some time to get to the hospital.'

'I don't suppose I could meet your sister?' Auntie Sal had previously told Linda of her wish to meet Marianna, and this was the reason why she had come with Linda and the Conde to see Alice and pick her up. But Auntie Sal had not really expected to be able to go to the hospital, not when there were three visitors already. However, Duarte lifted his brows at the question and said at once,

'Of course you must meet Marianna. You're soon to be related, remember, and we are hoping you will come to Portugal for a holiday quite soon.'

He paused. 'How about extending your visit when you come for the wedding?'

Auntie Sal was delighted and it showed.

'Thank you for that invitation, Duarte. I shall most certainly take you up on it!'

Linda was happy about the invitation too. It would be so nice to have her aunt over for a week or two, and it would undoubtedly be a pleasant change for her.

Marianna was sitting up in bed, her very dark head against the pillows. Linda had been shown photographs of her and had thought her beautiful, but as she looked down into the delicately-fashioned features she realised that the photographs had not done anything in the way of flattery.

'I'm so happy to meet you, Linda. I'd naturally wondered what you were like but Alice has assured me that my children have taken to you.' Strangely she seemed a little shy, which surprised Linda, since she was nearly twenty-nine, three years older than Linda. 'And now, you are to marry my brother. . . .' Her dark brown eyes lifted to the man standing there, a half-smile hovering on his lips to give him that hint of urbane charm which flickered through every now and then and which never failed to set Linda's pulses quickening above their normal rate.

Why had Marianna stopped? Somehow, Linda felt sure she was thinking of Lucia, whom Duarte's family had been expecting him to marry.

'I shan't be at the wedding—' Marianna glanced

up again at her brother. 'You did say, on the telephone, that you had no intention of delaying?'

Linda flashed him a look. He had not said anything to her about rushing the wedding. However, his expression was one of firm decision as he answered his sister.

'Naturally we'd have wished you to be at our wedding, Marianna, but despite the favourable report concerning your progress, it's still not certain just when you'll be coming home. Linda and I are to be married within the month.'

A little startled, Linda widened her eyes unconsciously. But on noting his set expression which plainly forbade any comment, she prudently kept her silence.

And in any case, she herself had no wish to wait. . . .

# Chapter Seven

The ceremony, and the ensuing reception, had gone off without a hitch, but with Linda's mind in a turmoil—not of doubt for she still knew that feeling of tranquillity at having made the right decision. But she was living through the day in a state of unreality, as if she had been carried on a magic carpet to some other realm where she was no longer responsible for her actions. Others were thinking for her; she played her part in the ceremony as if she were a puppet on a string. Yet through it all—the wedding itself, the reception in the Small Hall of the Palacio, the final departure of the guests—she was profoundly conscious of the seriousness of the step she was taking. She could not deny that the physical aspect had had much to do with her decision in the first place, for undoubtedly the Conde's magnetism had drawn her, making her aware of him as a man, making her aware of herself as a woman . . . a woman who was no longer fulfilled and who, though still loyal in heart and mind to those who had gone, had freely to admit that she was missing something vitally important . . . sex.

And now, as she stood by the dressing-table brushing her hair while she waited for her bridegroom, she experienced a feeling of expectancy, of exhilaration, so that when presently he appeared, seen through the mirror, she was ready for him . . . and willing.

He did not smile; on the contrary, it seemed that there was the hint of a frown between the eyes that subjected her to a prolonged scrutiny.

Were his thoughts with his lost love? Linda had already considered the possibility of their both pretending that they were being made love to by *someone else*. The idea was abhorrent but not lightly to be dismissed. However, now that her husband was here with her, she knew that, for herself, Duarte would be the one making love to her . . . only Duarte.

But what about him? He said softly,

'You look very beautiful, Linda. . . .' and his voice trailed. Again she asked herself where his thoughts were.

'Thank you,' she responded, laying down the silver-backed brush. The set had been a present from her aunt a few years ago, and Auntie Sal had been so pleased to see it there, on Linda's dressing-table.

'You can have a gold one now,' the old lady had said.

'I prefer this one, Auntie. I shall always have it here, and use it.'

Her aunt was here, in the Palacio, occupying a suite which had made her exclaim, on being shown into it by her niece,

'My—but this is luxury indeed! My Linda, this is something I never visualised would be for me! I shall feel like the Queen in here!'

The recollection brought the glimmer of a smile to Linda's lips and she heard her husband say,

'Something is amusing you. Would you care to share it with me.' Duarte, in a brocade gown of crimson and black, took a couple of steps forward and closed the communicating door behind him.

'I was thinking of Auntie and her delight at the suite you said she must have. Duarte,' she went on seriously and herself taking a step which brought her closer to him, 'thank you for being so very kind to Auntie Sal. This is something wonderful for her; she has never had much in the way of luxuries in her life—and certainly not since she was widowed. She is going to love this holiday you are giving her.' Serious the tone, limpid the eyes which she lifted to his.

'There is no need to thank me,' he returned, already having made a swift, dismissive gesture with one slender brown hand. 'Your aunt is now a relative of mine so naturally I give her the best. It's my duty to do so.' He moved again, and held out his hands. The sense of expectancy increased within her; she felt a little breathless, and more than a little shy.

She could not speak, but the dawning of a smile touched her lips and eyes. Duarte came to her, infinite understanding in his deeply penetrating gaze. Falteringly she put her hands in his, felt their strength and warmth and her smile deepened. Unafraid, she allowed herself to be drawn towards him until their bodies touched, hers clad in a filmy nightgown, gossamer light and more transparent than she had noticed at the time she bought it.

They stood together for several seconds in silence. Then Duarte murmured something in Portuguese and, bending his head, he kissed his wife on the lips. She quivered against him, still shy yet still unafraid. Hesitantly she slid her hands over the smooth silk of the dressing-gown to let her fingers meet at the back of his neck. He was faintly startled by the gesture, but it seemed to put him at his ease and stimulate him at the same time, so that his second kiss was far less restrained than the first. His hands were at her waist, squeezing the flesh, and his foreign voice was as smooth as silk as he said,

'You're very desirable, Linda. . . .' Was it imagination, she wondered, or was he really a long way from her, detached yet fully aware of the situation which he was in?

A sigh that was almost a sob rose from the depths of her as fleetingly doubts flashed unwanted into her mind.

Had she done the right thing?

His dark eyes lowered to her face, and it seemed as if he sensed her unease for his arm went about her and tightened, drawing her to him. His lips met hers and locked for long moments before beginning to explore. He kissed her throat and her shoulder, her temple. Sensations slowly spread over her, familiar and yet, paradoxically, new. His lips were moist, masterfully demanding her own to part for his tongue to push deeply into the smooth dark hollow of her mouth. She felt its tip run tantalisingly round the inside of her cheeks, setting alight the first glimmering flame of desire. Instinctively she arched against him and again the eager response seemed to surprise him. She noticed the expression flash into his eyes and, with a little access of embarrassment, she drew away. It afforded him an opportunity to move the narrow ribbon straps from her shoulders; she coloured and averted her eyes. Gently he tilted her chin and she saw the luminous quality of his gaze, the unmistakable sign of desire. She swallowed as he slid a hand beneath the bodice of the nightgown and cupped a breast in strong smooth fingers. His palm against her was like silk as it shaped itself to the lower curve, while the fingers moved to squeeze and tempt, to tease the nipple until it was hard and pointed within his grasp. She closed her eyes when presently he lowered the nightgown to the floor. She felt hot with embarrassment for, somehow, she had not expected to have her nightgown removed. She had felt that, the marriage being what it was, she would have been allowed a little modest covering. But now she was naked before him and she opened her eyes to see him removing his dressing-gown. But he had pyjamas on beneath it and these he made no attempt to take off. She heard the throaty accents as, bringing her close with hands that slid smoothly down her spine, he said against her breast,

'Don't be shy, Linda. We are married, dear.'

Dear. . . . Linda knew for sure that it meant nothing, being merely a figure of speech that happened to fit to what he was saying.

'Yes,' she murmured in response, her face buried in the curve of his shoulder. 'Yes . . . we're married.'

His hands began moving over her body, from gentle strokes on her neck and shoulder, down to her breasts and on to the slender waist and the delectable curves below it. Nerves tingled and senses strummed as his fingers, reaching her lower curves, curled sensuously inwards to find the tender place and set her body on fire with longing. His mouth on hers was gentle at first, but as his own desires were fuelled by her reciprocation to the sudden rhythmic swaying of his granite strong frame it became almost ruthless in its mastery and demands. Her own moist lips were forced apart; she knew the thrill of his tongue again, rough against the inside rim of her lips. His hand was now on her breast, fingers demanding that the nipples should stand out erect and firm, an invitation to his mouth which closed about the soft white flesh, and his tongue caressed the taut little bud, unceasing, insistent, until Linda's arousal was complete as every nerve cell in her body became alive with erotic intensity, aflame with the primitive fire of longing.

Spasm after spasm of sheer rapture tore their wild, tempestuous way through her and she clung fiercely to him, her frenzied fingers digging into the flesh of his shoulders. Soon both his palms were low down, glued to her curves, bringing her to him so that she was alive to his need of her, and to the agonising ache of desire spreading through her loins like an outflow of molten lava. The room began to spin as moments passed, timeless moments which lifted her to dizzying heights then left her floating in a magic realm of blissful languour. And then she was spinning once more, ecstasy quivering beneath the expert manoeuvre of his hands and mouth and body. She inhaled the heady male smell of him as he swung her right off her feet, to carry her over to the bed where the covers had been turned back by the maid. For a long moment he let his eyes take their fill of her beauty, as she lay there on her back, staring up at him through eyes dreamy with desire. She turned her head, though, as he took off his pyjamas; she heard him snap off the bright light which left a romantic amber-peach filter of light from the cupid-held bed lamp.

She turned to him when he came beside her and for a long time thrilled to his love-play, finding that she herself could without embarrassment employ her hands, contributing to the delightful interlude. Both their bodies began to move in unison as the fervour increased and heaven was only a breath away. Linda's lips parted as rapture brought a little moan to the back of her throat, but his taking stifled it and she was soaring, weightless, into the clouds.

The following morning Linda awoke to the sun slanting in bright little darts of gold through the chinks in the curtains. For a few bewildered seconds she was dazed, then reality and recollection widened her eyes and she turned her head. Duarte was sleeping, his handsome face dark and tranquil, his hair most attractively tousled, with a curling lock lying on his forehead. She looked her fill, taking in the incredibly long lashes which any girl would have envied, the straight classical nose, the aristocratic lines of his jaw, the firm, resolute curve of the chin. He was in the very prime of life, she thought—mature without being even middle-aged, distinguished with but a few grey hairs on his head. He was less than three years older than she; the fact was most satisfying for she wanted him for always, and, had he been many years older than she, widowhood would inevitably been hers—a long period of widowhood.

He stirred and opened his eyes, as if compelled to do so by the intensity of her stare. Her lovely lips parted in a smile and Duarte responded.

'Didn't I say we would do very well together?' he murmured and she knew the words were in effect meant as a reassurance, just in case she were feeling embarrassed, or even just a tiny bit self-conscious. 'You've no regrets?' he added when she did not speak.

'No regrets, Duarte,' she smiled.

Leaning up on one elbow, he kissed her lightly on the lips. And then, almost abruptly, 'Time we were up. I can't remember having slept so late for a very long time.'

Auntie Sal had been up for over an hour when Linda came down and, seeing her on the terrace, she went out to her, hoping she was assuming a little more composure than she felt.

The old lady was standing by a lovely oleander bush, fingers touching a flower.

'There you are, love,' she smiled, turning her head. 'And you look happy.' The last word came slowly, doubtfully and Auntie Sal's throat moved as if she were swallowing convulsively. 'You are happy, dear?' she asked just as if she could not help it.

'As happy as I expected to be, Auntie.'

'But not totally happy?' It was a silly question and they both knew it.

'I didn't expect too much,' replied her niece gently. 'I'm lucky,' she added reflectively. 'I have the chance to be a mother again.'

Her aunt nodded mechanically.

'I hope it won't be too long, dear, before you begin to raise a family, for it will be then that you'll really begin to forget.'

'I shan't ever forget, Auntie Sal, you know that.'

'The pain though—? It'll get less and less.'

'I believe it will. Duarte assures me it will and he should know. He's had a loss too, as I told you.'

'He wasn't married, though, with children.'

'No, but he was very deeply in love.'

A deep sigh escaped the old woman.

'Life is sad—and fate cruel to us,' she murmured. And then, with a sudden frown, 'Why are we talking like this? It was I who started it! And it isn't as if I woke up feeling blue—on the contrary. What a delightful place this is! And what a lovely wedding you had yesterday! Everything is fine and wonderful and I'm a silly old woman to let my spirits flag like that!'

Impulsively Linda put an arm around her shoulders and gave her a little squeeze.

'You always were a worrier,' she admonished, but with an affectionate quality to her voice. 'You have to admit, darling, that things have changed miraculously in the past few weeks.'

'How right you are! Tell me, love, how long am I to stay? I don't want to be a nuisance—'

'Auntie Sal—you've only been here a few days. There's no question of your overstaying your welcome, if that is what you are thinking. Duarte wants you to stay as long as you like.'

'He said that?' The old woman looked rather expectantly at her.

'Not in so many words, but I know he wants you to stay until you yourself feel you want to go home.' Linda was remembering how her aunt loved to be alone—'doing my own thing without having to please anyone else.' Now, though, if her expression were anything to go by, she very much wanted to make her stay at the Palacio a long one.

125

'It's so beautiful,' murmured the old woman as if aware of what Linda was thinking. 'And my suite— well, it is just unbelievably lovely.'

'I must take you to the Casa later today,' suggested Linda who was so eager to get started that, now the wedding was over, she intended to concentrate on the task of putting it right. Duarte said she would have a free hand to do whatever she liked. And Linda had discussed the renovations with Marianna so had a good idea that her own choice would be very suitable to her sister-in-law's taste.

'What you suggest sounds fine,' Marianna had said. 'I am sure it'll all look charming when you have finished with it.'

Duarte had said that he would give Linda a list of firms who would carry out her orders. Cost was not to be considered.

'Yes, I'd like to see the home which Marianna will come to,' mused Auntie Sal. 'I can tell Alice all about it; she'll be very interested as you can guess.' The pale blue eyes smiled and Linda suddenly wished her aunt would stay here at the Palacio for a long time . . . in fact, make her home here.

Duarte said Linda must use one of the cars to drive her aunt over to the Casa, this after she had said they intended walking.

'It's too far,' he had asserted, suggesting they have the chauffeur drive them over.

'But I don't like keeping him waiting, Duarte,' she had returned. 'Auntie and I could be there for a long time.' She made a wry face. 'You see, I want to begin making plans right away.'

He nodded his approval and it was then that he said she could take one of the cars.

'You're a lucky girl, really,' murmured her aunt as they drove along the mile-long avenue which constituted the drive of the Palacio. There was no mistaking the implication of the word 'really'; it spoke plainly of the old lady's regret that this wasn't a love match.

On arrival at the Casa, and even before she had alighted from the car Auntie Sal was heard to give a gasp of appreciation.

'It's really lovely!' she exclaimed when she was out of the car and staring up at the pillared front façade.

'That's just what I said when I first saw it. I'm just dying to get started on it!'

Her aunt looked at her.

'You did say you were nervous at first.'

'Of the responsibility? Yes, I was; it seemed a colossal task and one I wasn't capable of.'

'But now you've changed your mind, it would seem?'

Linda nodded and said ruefully,

'I had to. Duarte wouldn't take no for an answer.'

It was her aunt's turn to nod her head.

'Alice said he was the bossy type and I reckon she was right. Don't let him domineer you too much, child. It might be exciting when you're young but, later, when you begin wanting to make a life for yourself, being dictated to can pall.'

Linda said nothing, but if she had it would have

been to assure her aunt that she would never want to 'make a life for herself'—at least, not one which did not include her husband in its entirety.

The two wandered in the grounds first, and Linda was pleasantly surprised at the constructive suggestions her aunt made regarding reshaping some areas of the gardens, especially those close to the house.

They then went inside, and again Auntie Sal was helpful with her ideas.

'You almost make me wish I would be here to see the finished product,' she murmured with a wistful expression. 'However. . . .' She ended with a sigh which made Linda decide to ask Duarte if her aunt could stay on indefinitely.

This she did as soon as they were back at the Palacio.

'Of course,' he agreed at once. 'I thought I had already made it clear that your aunt could stay as long as she likes.'

Linda spoke to her aunt as they sat on the patio, at a white wrought-iron table, richly ornamented and with matching chairs, having afternoon tea that same day.

'You want me to stay indefinitely?'

'I'd love you to have a really long stay, Auntie. But I don't want to push you in any way. I know, though, that you'll make your own decision in the end,' she added finally, reaching for her aunt's cup and saucer so she could pour her more tea.

'I know I've always said I liked being on my

own,' reflected the old lady, 'but somehow I'd become used to having someone living in the house—you.' She threw her a rueful little glance. 'I have to admit, Linda, that I missed you after only a week. . . . Oh, at the very beginning it was fine, being on my own, without having to think of meals—'

'I always did suspect you neglected your food,' admonished her niece severely.

'Well, yes, I used to make a sandwich—you know how it is when you live alone.'

'But when I came you made nice meals, mainly to entice me to eat.' Linda paused a moment. 'So you became used to having a proper meal?'

The old woman nodded her head.

'That's right. But it wasn't only at mealtimes that I came to miss you, dear. I missed your presence in the house. It's difficult to explain, but there it is: I certainly wasn't as contented with my single way of living after you went as I was before you came.'

'And now?'

The old lady gave a shrug which was mostly one of resignation.

'I must get used to it again. But meanwhile—' She broke off and sent her niece a little smile of gratitude. 'Meanwhile, love, I'm going to accept your offer—and that of your husband—to stay for as long as I like.'

Linda was happy; she felt sure, somehow, that her aunt would eventually decide to make her home here, in Portugal. Linda knew though, that her aunt would still desire to be quite alone at times and, therefore, she would have to be provided with a suite of her very own. Linda decided not to talk to Duarte about this yet awhile, since there would be time for that if and when her aunt did come to a firm decision about her future.

# Chapter Eight

The three children were playing on the lawn at the back of the house. Auntie Sal, watching, tightened her mouth a little and, turning to her niece, said severely,

'That little madam wants chastising.'

Linda nodded but only to pacify the old lady. Clara was up to her tricks again, demanding that she have the ball kicked to her more often, and in a less boisterous way.

'I'm only a girl!' she cried stamping her foot. 'Felix, it's you who are doing it . . . !' She went off into Portuguese and it was at that moment that her uncle appeared on the scene.

'Clara!'

She looked his way, coloured up then turned her back on him. Linda caught her breath, wondering what Clara had said when she spoke just now in her own language.

With swift and purposeful strides Duarte covered the distance between him and his niece and, seizing her by the arms, he shook her thoroughly. She closed her lips tightly, to hold back the tears which threatened, surmised Linda.

'Now go to your room,' commanded her uncle. 'And stay there until I give you permission to leave it.'

Linda frowned and asked what the child had said.

'She called her brother a stupid idiot.' Duarte's voice was sharp with anger. 'You were right,' he said turning to Auntie Sal, 'when you said she deserved a spanking.'

'She's been spoiled, and I can't think why. Alice was very stern with them all from what I can gather.' Auntie Sal's eyes were following the child as she went towards the house, feet dragging.

'Marianna spoiled them, I'm afraid.' His eyes went to the two boys, standing close together and looking faintly upset that their sister was being punished. 'The boys don't appear to have been affected in any adverse way, but Clara's always been headstrong. However, she isn't going to be allowed to be insolent—not to anyone.' His stern gaze was on the dejected little figure and Linda, despite her agreement that Clara had to be punished, felt her heart go out to her. If she had had a father perhaps she would have been different, but her father had deserted them all and in consequence there must inevitably be some reaction. Linda said musingly,

'You don't know what goes on in her mind, Duarte. I'm sure there's something psychological in it; she probably misses her father.'

He nodded but said brusquely,

'She has to be made aware, though, that people are not to be insulted.'

'It's a pity about the break-up of the marriage.' Auntie Sal was thinking of Alice and of how upset she had been when Marianna's husband left her for another woman.

'In a way, yes,' conceded Duarte but after a pause he added, 'Marianna deserved someone better. The man she was betrothed to has never married. If and when the divorce takes place I rather think he will begin courting my sister again.' He seemed pleased by his own thoughts and all the anger had dissolved. He smiled from one to the other, excused himself, and left them by the fountain where they had stopped to watch the children playing their ball game.

'He'll be a stern father,' predicted Auntie Sal as she watched his tall, athletic figure disappearing from view around the side of the Palacio.

'But a just one.'

'I think you've already made a sort of hero out of him,' declared her aunt with a hint of amusement.

Mechanically Linda nodded her head.

'Who could help it, Auntie. He *is* something rather special; you must agree with me?'

'Yes, I do.'

'I wonder what this suitor of Marianna's is like?' said Linda, changing the subject. 'It would be wonderful if she were to get married again, to someone who would be faithful this time.'

'As you know, Alice doesn't divulge much about her one-time employer or her family, but she did once mention this man to me . . .' Her voice trailed as she tried to recall his name. Eventually the puckered forehead cleared. 'Henrique, yes, that's his first name. I don't remember his other names,' went on the old lady ruefully, 'because they're as long as those of the Conde. He's a Marquez something-or-other.' Auntie Sal allowed herself a whimsical smile. 'All these titles! And you and I just ordinary people. What strange tricks fate does play on us!'

'I agree,' reflectively from Linda whose thoughts very naturally fled back in time to those wonderful days when there were four of them . . . a happy family, a typical family with struggles and problems where money was concerned, a family who *noticed* a particular little luxury that came their way. Whereas here, on this vast *quinta* where money seemed to flow unhindered from some hidden source, luxury was the norm, something so customary that even the three children took it for granted.

'The dramatic change in your life and your circumstances.' Her aunt looked sideways at her niece and there was an odd quality of gentleness in her voice when next she spoke. 'You deserved the break, Linda, dear. Not many have it as tough as you, as sad.'

Linda looked at her and contrived a smile.

'It's as Duarte said, Auntie; the pain is fading.'

'I too said it would,' her aunt reminded her, not to be outdone. 'I said that you'd recover if only you'd do something. Get out, meet people, find a job, but . . .' She stopped and frowned her dislike of what she had been about to say, but Linda finished for her, in a self-deprecating little voice,

'. . . instead of sitting there all day, brooding and wanting to die.' She frowned as she paused. 'I see now that it was stupid, Auntie, but at the time—well, I just couldn't manage to snap out of it.'

'Not until you came here. Now, though, you have a new life, and as you said, there'll be children for you to love and who will love you.'

Linda nodded, wondering if she and Duarte and the children that were to come would form a happy family of the kind she had known before. She and her husband had been deeply in love when they married, and that love had grown deeper with the passing years. . . .

This marriage was in reality one of convenience for both Duarte and herself, and there had been no love between them. . . .

Had been. . . . Now? Undoubtedly she was drawn to the nobleman who was her husband, the man with the spectacular good looks and superlative physique. She delighted in his company, thrilled to his smile, enjoyed his love-making. Surely all this was beginning to spell . . . love. . . . It was not the first time she had said that to herself.

\* \* \*

The following morning Linda and her aunt went over to the Casa de Rialta. Linda had a notebook and pencil, and was writing busily, already able to see the result of some of the renovations. But half of her mind was on what Duarte had said about Marianna's previous suitor, the man with whom a marriage had been arranged. If it should transpire that he and Marianna got married, then all these renovations would be for nothing. Linda had in fact ventured to mention this to her husband and had been given the perfectly logical reply.

'We can't see that far ahead, Linda. I must have a home ready for my sister to occupy immediately she returns to Portugal. She wouldn't want to stay here, in the Palacio, not with the children. They need to have their own home. If it should transpire that Henrique is still interested in marriage to my sister, which as you know I believe he is, then the Casa might have to be rented out to a suitable tenant. However, we don't know how Marianna will feel about Henrique.' Duarte looked at his wife and frowned a little as he added, 'She turned him down once, remember.'

'But must now regret it, Duarte,' returned Linda reasonably.

'Perhaps; yet women are unpredictable. When I talked with Marianna in the hospital she seemed very upset at the failure of her marriage.'

'She would—any woman would. But that doesn't say she'd have him back, surely.'

'No, I don't think for one moment she would. She seems resolved to divorce him, but on the other hand, this doesn't automatically mean that

Marianna would be willing to marry the man she previously turned down.'

Linda had to agree, and now as she moved from the large and airy main room of the Casa she did wonder what was to be the ultimate fate of the beautiful house, for she felt sure that, one day, the lovely Marianna would find a wonderful husband.

'This is the dining-room, I suppose?' Auntie Sal was looking around appreciatively. 'What I like about these rooms, Linda, is their size. They're small in comparison to those of the Palacio—more manageable, if you know what I mean?'

'Yes, I certainly do,' agreed her niece. 'When I first came to the Palacio it seemed that the rooms were enormous but I'm used to them now and love them. But, as you say, the rooms here are—well —homely. . . .' She paused, feeling she had not made the point accurately for despite the size of the rooms at the Palacio they did not in any way lack warmth and homeliness. 'I suppose you are thinking that, for you, these rooms would be preferable?'

The old lady nodded at once.

'I could be very happy and cosy in this house, Linda.' There was a wistful note in her voice which brought a slight frown to Linda's forehead. She had not thought that her aunt would like to live in what was relative splendour. Yet was this house really splendid? It was a much, much smaller version of the Palacio and she could almost see her aunt installed—Linda cut her thoughts. This house would be far too large for one person.

137

'I'm thinking of having blue and gold decorations in here,' she said after a long silence. 'Blue walls—light blue—and gold trimmings to these carved flowers on the cornice.'

Auntie Sal looked up at the ornamental moulding running all around the room just below the ceiling.

'That should look lovely,' she agreed. 'What furniture are you having?'

'The dining chairs will have seats upholstered in blue tapestry, and I shall have the window-seat upholstered to match.' Her eyes went to the large bay window jutting out to a wide patio, overrun now with unwanted vegetation but easily seen in all its previous glory when its columns were gleaming white and dripping with flowers.

'And the drapes will be blue, I think?'

'That's right.' They went from the dining-room to what had been the study but which would now be a living-room—a smaller version than the main room whose decor and furnishings had already been planned by Linda, with the whole-hearted approval of her aunt.

'I love this room.' Auntie Sal went on to suggest it be done in white, with red damask lounge suite and occasional chairs to match. Linda thought this a good idea and became busy with notebook and pencil again.

'How long is it all going to take?' inquired the old lady, looking rather doubtfully at her niece. 'Will it be ready for Marianna to occupy as soon as she comes home?'

'I think so.' She made a wry face. 'I guess Duarte can get things done without much delay.'

And she was right. In moved the workmen and at the same time the Palacio gardeners tackled the grounds. Linda went with her aunt to town to order the furniture, to employ a firm to fit carpets and curtains once the workmen and the decorators moved out.

'It's exciting, all this hustle and bustle!' exclaimed Linda's aunt. 'Oh, I know what you're thinking—looking surprised as you are doing at this moment! You're thinking how I used to love the quiet, uneventful life. Well, this is such a change for me, a real novelty! I love being part of it and I shall have so much to tell Alice when I get back. . . .' Her voice quivered away to nothing and, looking at her swiftly, Linda again saw that wistful expression on her pale, lined face. Briskly she changed the subject, talking about the coming vintage, trying to take her aunt's mind off the thought of going home.

'The vintage? It's soon?'

'It takes place in autumn, so it's not long now.'

'I'll be interested,' eagerly from her aunt, and Linda found herself smiling affectionately at her. This was a different Auntie Sal altogether—a brighter, younger one, showing enthusiasm never before seen by her niece. 'I've read about the vintage and it's fun from what I can gather.' She and Linda were again at the Casa, watching the drapes being put up in the large saloon. 'This transformation's been done so swiftly—but you did say your husband would get things done in a hurry if he was so minded, and it seems he was.'

'He's anxious for it to be ready for Marianna. I did tell you she's coming home in about three weeks, didn't I?'

'Yes, dear. I'm so glad for her. She oughtn't to have to endure hardships, being who she is, of the nobility.'

'Well, once she's back here, with her own people, she'll soon forget the past—and her illness. No one could be unhappy in a beautiful place like this.'

Her aunt shot her a glance.

'No,' she murmured with quiet significance, 'no one could be unhappy here.'

That evening after dinner Auntie Sal said she was tired and went to bed, leaving Linda and Duarte to have coffee and cognac in a small, intimate saloon whose window overlooked the miniature waterfall and ornamental pool. Delicately-coloured lamps concealed in the trees sent their quivering glow on to the pool, to shower its surface with the magical blending of colours. The drapes were drawn right back and Linda, facing the window, looked out and suddenly all was unreal and she felt like pinching herself, just to make sure she wasn't lost in a wonderful dream. The thought brought a smile hovering to her lips and she heard her husband say,

'What is it, Linda, that makes you smile?'

She turned to him, eyes limpid and wide, framed by long curling lashes which, in the shadows cast by a huge potted palm, sent dark reflections on to her cheeks. She noticed a nerve twitch in his jaw as he allowed his eyes to examine her face, then her throat, then the lovely curves so clearly outlined by the snugly-fitting evening blouse she wore.

'I was thinking just how my life has changed,' was her frank reply to his question. 'I was wondering if I really were awake,' she added with a tiny, self-deprecating laugh.

'You're awake, all right,' he assured her with a hint of amusement in his dark eyes. 'Tell me,' he added changing the subject, 'how is the Casa coming along? As you know, I've been too busy to go over this last week.'

'Oh, you'd not know it!' she answered eagerly. 'It's almost finished, and looking so beautiful! Auntie is always saying how perfect it is. She'd like to live in a house like that.'

Duarte smiled.

'I like your aunt, Linda.' A small pause and then, 'You know, she ought not to be living all on her own, so far away from her only relative. Wouldn't she like to live here?'

'Oh, Duarte! I've been thinking about it. But I felt it was too soon either to speak to you or Auntie about it. She isn't getting any younger, as you yourself once remarked, when you were asking me to marry you—remember?'

'I remember.' There was a quizzical look in his eyes and she blushed a little, aware that she had been voicing irrelevancies.

'Well, as we've agreed, she isn't getting any younger and so the time might come when she can't do as much for herself as she does now.' Linda paused thoughtfully, brandy glass in her hand. 'Do you suppose she could have her own apartment—if she did come to live with us, that is?'

'I should think that is possible. She would prefer that, you think?'

Linda nodded.

'She likes her own company—needs to be alone at times.'

'In that case, presupposing she does want to come here permanently, then we shall have to take a look around and see what can be done.' He paused in thought and Linda looked at his in profile and was, as always, vitally aware of him as a man. She was proud to be his wife, and all at once a surge of sheer joy sped through her veins and in the next few pulsing moments she became conscious of a wild sensation of longing . . . for what . . . ?

For him to love her? To fall as deeply in love with her as he had been with that other love of his?

And what of herself? Loyalty to her husband and children had many times to be brought deliberately to the forefront of her mind these days . . . because she was apt to forget.

Guilt would sweep over her; she would tell herself that loyalty must remain her chief emotion. But this man, this scion of the Portuguese nobility, often now engaged her whole mind to the exclusion of all else.

He seemed to have become her very life, the centre around which everything of importance revolved.

She heard him say at length,

'I should mention it to your aunt, Linda, see how she reacts.'

'You don't think it's too soon, then?'

'Not at all. She'll make up her own mind in any case. But it would certainly be reassuring to her to know that she can have a permanent home here if she wants.'

Linda looked gratefully at him. She would speak to her aunt tomorrow and get her reaction. Obviously the idea would require pondering over, since, if she did decide to move, Auntie Sal would have to sell most of her things, and the little house in which she had lived for so long.

And what of her friend, Alice? The two had known each other for a great many years and neither might be very enamoured with the thought that they might never meet again.

Duarte's quiet voice broke into her reverie and she glanced up.

'Would you care for a stroll, Linda?'

Her eyes lit up; she placed her glass on the table as she answered,

'I'd love to. It's a beautiful night.' Joy was spreading through her veins again but she felt she must at all costs put a rein on her feelings in case by a glance or a deeper expression of her eyes she should give herself away.

They went out through the French window, into the fresh night air, air scented with flowers and the more pungent smell of pines. Above, the star-sown heavens were a deep purple, with the moon like a silver boat sailing across them. All was silent but for the cascade of sparkling water and the gentle sough of the breeze, making the pine needles murmur like a soft and subtle whisper from a long way off.

Suddenly they were close, and she felt her husband's hand seeking hers. His fingers curled, warm and strong and possessive.

No words were spoken, but then there was no need. Silences between them had never been constrained, or even faintly awkward. Moonlight made a patchwork on the lawn, then seconds later all was hazy and mysterious as clouds spun a veil across the silver crescent.

Duarte stopped unexpectedly and stood above her, staring down into her eyes. They were close to a pretty little arbour and she would have moved to sit down but he stopped her with such sudden roughness that she widened her eyes, startled.

'I was going to sit down,' she murmured but he shook his head.

'Not here.' His voice seemed abrupt, thought Linda and for a moment bewilderment swept over her. But then she felt she knew why her husband did not want to sit there—with her. It was the little arbour where he used to take his first love. Here a couple could be hidden from all eyes, could kiss and embrace . . . and perhaps even be intimate. . . .

A chill swept over her and the illusion of happiness was fading.

'Let's go back,' she quivered. 'I've become— tired all of a sudden.' Her voice was flat; all the dreams she'd had for the future seemed to dissolve in this knowledge that had come to her. She felt a stranger in this adopted country . . . not really wanted.

Would Duarte's thoughts always wander back to his lost love? And yet, what right had she to dwell on the question, to resent—no matter how faintly —the fact that his thoughts should go sometimes to the girl whom he had loved so deeply that he could not offer love to any other woman? He had been honest with her, Linda, and likewise she had been honest with him: neither could love anyone but the one they had lost, they said. She herself often lived again the life she had known with her husband, and yet, here she was, half angry at what had just happened.

A deep sigh escaped her but her husband did not notice, and when she glanced upwards and side-ways at him she realised that his mind was a long way off. He was detached, not only from her but from his surroundings . . . except for that little arbour. . . . A shrine, here in the grounds of the Palacio, an everlasting memory of a lover who had died.

In the bedroom Linda undressed slowly, for the first time hoping Duarte would not come to her. She wanted to be alone with her thoughts even while she knew she would brood, on the past—her own past—among other things.

The nightgown was a dream of filmy silk and lace, a see-through creation which left nothing to the imagination of Duarte when presently he came into the room, dressing-gown partly open to reveal a strong brown chest where the hair seemed still damp and curly from the shower he had just taken. Body lotion was heady and pervasive, like the tang of wild vegetation on a tropical backshore. Vaguely she was wondering what particular brand it was.

'You're so beautiful,' he was saying and coming towards her slowly at the same time, his eyes dark and sensuous in their complete examination of her figure. Undoubtedly she appealed to him physically —but that was all. She was in effect his mistress, though she would be expected to bear him children, of course; nevertheless, she was little better than a woman picked up for the slaking of a man's pagan desires.

She tensed as he touched her, hands warm, and smooth as silk as they made feather-light strokes from her arms to her throat. The straps of the nightgown presented no obstacle for his exploring mouth as it followed the progress of his hands. He cupped her face, stared down into her eyes, then he bent his head and took possession of her lips. She tensed again, fully sensitive to the fact that her attitude was illogical, but yet unable to throw off the feeling of resentment . . . or was it jealousy? The idea was repulsive to her and she managed to shake it off, for how could she be jealous of someone who was dead?

Yet she heard herself say, drawing away from her husband's masterful and proprietorial hold on her scantily-clad body,

'Duarte—I don't want—I mean—I d-don't feel like—like. . . .'

His eyes registered surprise and then inquiry.

'You don't feel well?' He sounded anxious, she thought.

'No, it isn't that. . . .' she tailed off lamely and averted her face. With a peremptory little jerk he compelled her to look at him again and now she saw that his eyes were narrowed, the lids heavy above them. His strong mouth was set, that noble jaw thrust out. She caught her breath, never having seen him in this mood before. He was angry . . . and becoming angrier with every moment of her prolonged silence. 'It's—well, I don't want you tonight, Duarte.' There, it was out, and not very subtly—or delicately!—put.

Another silence, this time one of disbelief not unmingled with the hint of a threat. She realised that he had come to her almost ready for the satisfaction she could give him and that he was now both frustrated and humiliated. She hadn't been very wise.

'What, might I ask,' said her husband at last, 'is the reason for this sudden—aversion you have for me?'

She shook her head in instant protest.

'It's not aversion,' she denied.

'No?' A straight dark eyebrow was lifted. 'Perhaps you will explain, then?' he invited in tones both terse and commanding.

She was hot all over, unconsciously clutching the front of her nightgown in fingers that moved convulsively. This man with his cold-blooded appraisal and his glacier expression was not the kind and gentle one she had known up till now. This was an altogether different side of his nature . . . one she feared and disliked intensely.

'Duarte. . . .' There was a silent entreaty for understanding in the wide and limpid eyes she raised to his. 'Tonight—I can't—'

'And why?' The very brevity of the query threw her further into confusion and she freed her chin from his hold and turned away.

'I can't explain.' Her answer was almost as brief, but not accepted with the same meek reaction as she had shown. Duarte reached out and gripped her wrist, jerking her around to face him again. His face was tense and white; she feared he had taken her attitude as an insult . . . and the exalted Conde Duarte Alfonso Lourenco de Domingo was totally unused to insults.

'So you can't explain?' His voice was as formidable as his expression. 'You don't want me tonight but you haven't any explanation as to why.'

She was silent. How could she say that his manner out there, by the little arbour, had wrought this dramatic change in her attitude towards him? How could she, when she herself owned quite freely that it was all very illogical?

She shook her head, opened her mouth to speak then closed it again. Perhaps it was this small almost unconscious gesture that proved to be the spark which lit the real fire of his anger. Without affording her the chance of speaking, even if she could now find something to say, he brought her roughly to him and crushed her lips with his own. She began to struggle, which again was not very wise. Her slender, resisting body was forced against his corded hardness, her lips possessed once more, this time with almost brutal strength and she would have cried out in protest if she could.

'You made a bargain with me,' he reminded her almost harshly when at last he drew his mouth from hers. 'Do you suppose I shall allow you to change your mind?' His voice was calm but the anger came through, vibratingly clear. Yes, he had been humiliated and this was the cause of his wrath.

'I haven't changed my mind,' she faltered, having to cling to him or she was sure she would have fallen, so weak were her legs. Tears glistened on her lashes but although he noticed his manner underwent no change. 'It is just tonight, Duarte. I feel—strange—'

'In what way?' His tone was curt and glacier cold.

'I've said I can't explain.' She tried to draw away but his strength reduced her puny efforts to an absurdity.

In any case, she still felt weak, and drained by the feeling of deep depression that had come over her.

'You've decided you made a mistake in marrying me? Is that it?' He held her now at arms' length, his eyes flicking her body with a hint of contempt before settling disconcertingly on her face.

'No,' she protested, 'it isn't anything like that at all!'

He shook his head in puzzlement. Her tear-dimmed eyes, the tremulous movement of her mouth, the convulsive clutching of her fingers against the front of her nightgown . . . all these compounded to soften him a little, to urge him to press for an explanation.

'What is it, then, Linda?' he asked in a gentler tone. 'You must be able to tell me what is wrong?'

She began to shake her head then stopped. Within her something changed; she stared up at him, blinking to hold back the tears, and was just about to explain it all to him when he said, dawning enlightenment in his eyes,

'It's your husband. I see it now.' He paused but went on after a fleeting moment, giving her no chance to speak. 'You're reviving memories; you're thinking of your husband.' Again he paused but this time she had no wish to speak. 'If I were to make love to you it would be he who was in your thoughts.' Something like bitterness edged his voice but, strangely, there was no sign of reproach. 'That's your reason for not wanting me tonight.' He let go of her arms. 'Thank you,' he said in a toneless voice. 'I appreciate your reluctance. Good night, Linda. Sleep well—'

'Duarte—don't go! It wasn't like that—'

'I said good night.' Abrupt the tone now as he turned from her and moved towards the high communicating door between his room and hers. 'It's not your fault. No one can help their thoughts wandering.' He was at the door, his hand on the ornate brass knob. 'Don't let it keep you awake,' he said over his shoulder and the next moment the door had closed behind him.

Linda stood there staring for a long time, tears streaming down her cheeks. Through her own fault she had been misjudged, and she knew a terrible access of despair for she felt certain she would never ever be able to convince Duarte that he had been wrong in his conclusions. If only she had been quicker in reaching the stage where she could explain! It was ironical that he should judge her in the same way she had judged him. And if he were mistaken—which of course he was—then she could be mistaken too. She had taken much for granted, concluding that he had not wanted his wife to go to that little arbour because it had been his sacred place, the place where he could go when he wished to revive a memory. She, Linda, had no proof that this was what he was thinking; and hadn't she already told herself that her attitude was illogical?

Fool that she was! And to say she didn't want her husband when now, at this moment, she would have given anything to be in his arms, to thrill to his lips on hers, his body taking, and giving, in pleasure if not in love, and certainly in gentleness.

She looked away from the closed door and then back again. Should she knock and go in to him? Would he listen? More important, would he believe her?

Perhaps in any case he no longer had the desire to make love to her.

A deep sigh issued from her lips and her throat felt tight. She had been so happy earlier in the day, and all through dinner when her aunt had seemed so happy too.

And now. . . . Linda swallowed hard, made a move towards the door, then, with the conviction that nothing would come of humbling herself, she got into bed. But she soon realised that sleep was to elude her and she rose again and went to the window. The night outside was balmy and she stepped on to the balcony.

A figure met her eyes as she looked down to the terrace. Duarte. . . . Crossing the lawn in slacks and a sweater. Crossing in the direction of the far park from where, if he went far enough, he would reach that little arbour. . . .

# Chapter Nine

Auntie Sal frowned at her niece and bluntly asked what was wrong. Feigning bewilderment, Linda answered with little or no hesitation,

'The matter, Auntie. Nothing at all. Why do you ask?'

The old lady's eyes narrowed.

'Why? Because there's a darned mighty change in you, my girl, since last evening.'

'Perhaps I'm tired. I don't always sleep well.' She turned away and went to the sideboard to help herself to bacon and an egg which had been put there by Ricardo, one of the manservants who had asked Linda if he could serve her, but she had said she wasn't ready and would serve herself. Auntie Sal was already at the breakfast table and making a hearty meal—or had been until her niece walked in and she noticed the pallid skin and the shadowed eyes, swollen a little. . . .

'Something gone wrong between you and Duarte?' asked Auntie Sal, bypassing Linda's excuse.

'No, nothing.'

'He usually has breakfast with us,' she reminded her.

'I expect he was especially busy this morning. I know he has a lot to do at this time. For one thing, Marianna will be here shortly and for another it's almost time for the vintage.'

Her aunt's eyes wore a sceptical look but she refrained from any further comment on Duarte's absence. Nevertheless, it was clear that she was troubled; Linda realised this and a sigh escaped her. She had no wish for her aunt's holiday to be spoiled by anxiety regarding her niece's marriage.

'Are we going over to the Casa?' Auntie Sal changed the subject, her eyes focused on the view from the window and the wide lawn where the three children were playing prior to going to school. 'There's very little to do now, is there?'

'Just a bit of finishing off, the little touches like including a few more ornaments and mirrors. Marianna will have her own personal things so I'm not buying much in the way of extras.'

'I'm looking forward to seeing Marianna. Oh, I don't know her well, but she seemed so charming and, I suppose she is now a relative of mine?'

Linda smiled.

'You've suddenly acquired quite a number of relations, Auntie. Do you like the idea?'

'I love it! So long as you and Duarte are happy

then it's all right.' She looked directly at her across the table. 'Try dear, won't you?'

'Of course.'

'What I mean is—you mustn't always be recalling that other life because I rather think that Duarte's perception is pretty acute.'

Linda made no response. She was naturally thinking of last night when her husband had concluded she was captive to the invasion of memories. She ought to have disillusioned him at once, but though denial had reached her mind it had not reached her voice; her throat had been too choked for speech, her mouth too dry. Now, though, she knew a penetrating stab of regret for her attitude. She had made no attempt to put things right between them, and so her husband had reacted in the only way she would have expected. In every aspect his manner had portrayed a quality of arrogance, as if he were determined to vanquish the humiliation he had suffered at her hands. A humiliation she had never meant to inflict at all.

And this morning he had deliberately avoided a meeting with her. . . .

Her spirits were still flagging when a short while later she and her aunt were driving over to the Casa, and it was a strain on the nerves for her to appear cheerful.

'It looks so different!' Auntie Sal was exclaiming as they entered the hall of the Casa after Linda had unlocked the heavy oaken door. 'You're a genius, love!'

Linda turned to her with a swift smile.

155

'You planned some of it, remember.'

'Well . . . a little,' agreed her aunt, eyes lighting up at the praise. 'It was fun!'

At dinner that evening Duarte informed them that his sister would be home by the week-end.

'I shall be going over on Thursday to fetch her,' he added in a coolly impersonal voice that brought a frown to Auntie Sal's brow.

'The Casa is ready for occupation,' returned Linda.

'Good. Everything seems to be working out just right.'

'Shall you be back on Friday?'

'I hope so. Marianna will stay here for the first night, then you can help her settle in when she's ready.'

'She'll be needing servants,' from Auntie Sal, and Duarte said that Luisa would be sent from the Palacio for the time being.

'Marianna will want to engage her own staff,' he added after a small pause. He had already told Linda that Marianna would not be having any financial worries now that she was coming back to her own country. No explanation was given but Linda suspected that he was making over to her some of the inheritance she had lost when she defied her father and married an Englishman instead of the man chosen for her.

As on one or two previous occasions Auntie Sal said she was tired and went to bed early.

'I have work to do,' said Duarte only a short while later. 'So I'll bid you good night.' Cool the tone but not hostile in any way. He understood, was what he meant to convey to her. Yes, he fully understood that she was bound to think of her late husband at times of intimacy with her second husband.

How wrong he was! But how was she to tell him so now that she had acted so foolishly last night?

When he had gone to his study she wandered in the grounds for a while but she was restless and unhappy. Sleep would most likely elude her, she decided, but went indoors just the same, and up to her room.

Her husband would not come to her tonight, she knew, and tears filled her eyes.

No use putting off the truth any longer—stupid in fact, since she had known deep within her subconscious that she had been in love with her husband almost from the first. . . .

Marianna looked radiant, sitting there on the patio with her children around her—Clara squatting at her feet and the two boys standing one on each side of her.

'Smile, please!' from Auntie Sal. 'This has to be a good one as it's for Alice.'

'Oh, but it's so good to be home!' Marianna was exclaiming half an hour later as she played hostess to her two guests. The children had been taken off to play in the small enclosure where swings and slides had been erected on the instructions of Duarte. 'This house is lovely, Linda! Thank you so very much for all the trouble you've taken.'

'Auntie Sal helped,' inserted Linda and so the old lady was thanked too, beaming with pleasure.

'It was such fun—a new interest for me,' she said.

'You live alone, Linda was telling me.'

'Yes, I do.'

'It isn't good to live alone, Auntie Sal.'

Both of Marianna's guests glanced up swiftly. The 'Auntie Sal' had slipped out so naturally and to Linda it seemed more than ever only right that her aunt should make her home here. But as yet she hadn't broached the subject; the right moment seemed not to have presented itself. But now it had and Linda found herself saying gently,

'Marianna's right, you know. Why don't you make your home here—'

'My home! Permanently?' Although the old lady had paled a little there was no mistaking the glimmer of eagerness in her eyes. 'But—well, your husband wouldn't want to be bothered with anyone like me,' she protested, though very mildly indeed.

'On the contrary,' returned her niece with a smile, 'Duarte is in full agreement that if you want to come here, and live at the Palacio, then you must.'

'You've already discussed it, then?' The quiver in the old lady's voice betrayed the emotion within her. 'You make it very tempting, Linda,' she added on a wistful note.

'Think about it,' advised Marianna looking at her empty cup and holding out her hand to have it passed to her. She poured more tea from a silver pot, and passed the cup and saucer back. 'It's a serious step, of course,' continued Marianna when neither of the others spoke. 'And it'll be a big upheaval, but in the end it'll be worth it because you'll have company when you want it.' Her voice, accented but beautifully toned, was quiet and faintly persuasive. 'I daresay Duarte will arrange your apartments so that you can have privacy whenever you prefer it.'

'I do like my own company sometimes,' mused Auntie Sal and, catching her niece's rueful glance she added, 'I used to want it all the time—or practically all the time, until Linda came to me. After that, although I told myself I would again enjoy being alone—if Linda should ever leave me, that was—I began to suspect I had changed in certain respects.'

No more was said at this time, because the old lady had gone quiet as if already she was thinking the matter over and trying to come to a decision.

The following morning Linda went over to the Casa alone, as her aunt said she wanted to write a letter to Alice. Marianna was in the garden cutting flowers and Linda walked over to stand beside her.

'I've brought you a housewarming present from Auntie and me,' she smiled. 'I don't know if you have the same custom here, but I expect you know that we have it in England. When anyone moves to a new home friends buy them housewarming presents.'

Marianna nodded as she let her eyes fall on the pretty parcel which Linda had in her hand.

'It's sweet of you both,' she said, accepting the

parcel. 'Thank you very much.' They strolled back to the house together, two girls who knew that a deep friendship was already established on firm foundations. Marianna had wanted to know all about the circumstances of the marriage and had welcomed the fact of having a new sister. She didn't get along too well with Inez, it seemed, although as far as Linda was concerned Inez was quite charming and had seemed pleased about the marriage of her brother with the girl from England. Linda rather thought that the children of Inez and those of Marianna didn't get along together and this had sometime in the past caused a certain coolness to creep into the sisters' relationship with one another.

Once in the small living-room Marianna opened her parcel, exclaiming as she held the exquisite little jade figure in her hand.

'It's really beautiful, Linda. Do thank your aunt for me—but I shall thank her myself when I come over to the Palacio tomorrow.'

'We found it in an antique shop the other day and thought you would like it.'

'I certainly do! It's delightful.' Marianna put it on the mantelpiece, changed her mind and placed it on a small antique table. 'No, maybe not there—' She picked it up and took it to the mantelpiece again. 'Those children of mine might knock it off the table.' She was plainly thrilled with it, for she continued to handle it for several seconds after she had found the right place for it.

'Some coffee?' she asked then and Linda said yes, she would love some coffee.

Marianna reached for the bell-rope and within half a minute Luisa was there, being told to make the coffee. Watching Marianna, Linda thought she detected much of the pride of the de Dominga family; the girl had many traits possessed by her brother, and indeed, by all her brothers. Inez, too, had the same innate pride, and the poise and assurance with which to give orders to servants and yet at the same time making sure not to exhibit unnecessary arrogance. There was an art in it, decided Linda on noticing the smile which Luisa gave her mistress after receiving the order, an art which she, Linda, did not suppose she would ever acquire.

It was over coffee that Marianna opened a small album to show Linda some snapshots of the children when they were much younger. Linda commented as she flicked the pages backwards. She came to some snapshots of Marianna on her own, then with a handsome young man. Another photograph was of a staggeringly beautiful girl with golden hair and pale skin . . . and for no valid reason Linda's nerves tensed and she found herself saying, through lips that had for no reason at all gone dry,

'Who is this, Marianna?'

'The young man with me? Oh, I was to have married him—it was arranged by our parents. He was willing but I rebelled. I wanted to choose for myself.' She leant over. 'He's good-looking, don't you think?'

Linda merely nodded her head and murmured,

'I meant—this other snap—this lovely girl . . . ?'

161

'That—' Marianna frowned and paused. 'I didn't realise it was there—'

'It's the girl whom Duarte loved.' A statement for she was so very sure.

'Yes,' admitted Marianna still frowning.

'She's incredibly lovely. It's no wonder Duarte can't forget her—' Linda pulled herself up, not having meant to speak her thoughts aloud.

'He can't forget her?' from Marianna with a deepening of the frown. 'He's probably not forgotten her completely, but he has certainly recovered from the hurt of her death.' She was distressed even though she knew the full story regarding her brother's marriage to this girl whose colour was fast receding from her cheeks.

'I feel he must always be affected by the memory of her,' Linda murmured, a sinking feeling in the pit of her stomach. For how could any man forget a creature so unbelievably beautiful as this? Mechanically she touched the picture, trailing her finger lightly over it.

'No, I can't agree,' stated Marianna and it was plain that she meant it. 'Time heals everything; there is no argument to that. In any case,' went on Marianna reflectively, 'Filipa would not have been right for him—'

'Not right? But he was madly in love with her.'

'Of course he was, and so he was blind. Filipa was never strong, not even as a child, and we all doubted very much that she would have been able to bear children even had she lived. Duarte was very young—only twenty-two—and he wouldn't be mature enough to look ahead to a time of disappointment when he was without an heir. Filipa was so beautiful that all the men fell for her; she chose Duarte and this in itself made him feel good and made him think he was luckier than the rest. Oh, I am sure he still remembers her with affection—'

'Deep affection,' Linda could not help inserting and after a small and frowning pause Marianna nodded her head reluctantly. 'Perhaps,' she conceded but went on to add, 'It doesn't mean that she is in his thoughts all the time, Linda. On the contrary, Duarte has long since learned to laugh again. He's older now and more mature, and if you ask me, he now knows that the marriage, could it have taken place, would by no means have been the perfect thing he imagined when he was a boy of twenty-two.'

The calm logic of all this began to have its affect on Linda and her spirits lifted somewhat. She looked at this new sister of hers and on impulse confided in her what had happened a few nights ago. Marianna listened intently, shaking her head a little as if in censure.

'You ought to have let him know he was wrong in his conclusions, Linda. Your marriage being what it is, you can't afford to have any unnecessary misunderstandings.'

'I know that,' admitted Linda with a regretful sigh. 'It was stupid of me to let him believe that his assumptions were true.'

Marianna looked at her, a half-smile hovering on her lips.

'You should be able to put it right,' she said firmly at last.

'Will he believe me?'

'Why shouldn't he believe you?'

'I didn't deny it at the time.'

'So now you feel he'll merely regard any explanation or denial as an untruth?'

Linda nodded at once.

'I feel sure he will.'

'Well,' commented her sister-in-law reasonably, 'you'll never know what his reaction will be if you don't invite it in the first place, will you?'

'No. . . .' Somehow, Linda could not visualise going to her husband and making a belated attempt to convince him that he was wrong in assuming she was thinking of her late husband and, therefore, she had no wish for Duarte to make love to her.

'I must try to find a way,' she murmured at last. 'It won't be easy.'

'Nothing will be easy until my brother falls in love with you,' was the quiet rejoinder from her sister-in-law, and Linda jerked erect in her chair. She put her coffee cup down on the saucer with a little bang.

'Marianna . . . oh, do you think . . . is it possible?'

'So I was right,' murmured Marianna, 'in thinking you're in love with Duarte.' A statement; Linda said yes, Marianna was right.

'It was inevitable,' from Marianna. 'He's so devastatingly attractive. Yes, you were bound to fall in love with him in spite of your, too, having memories of someone else.'

'It isn't that I want to forget altogether,' began Linda. 'But love for Duarte just came. . . .'

'Linda, dear,' said the other girl gently, 'you're not the only woman to fall in love a second time. And neither will my brother be the first man. Go to him, Linda, and tell him everything—how you somehow concluded he was keeping you from that arbour intentionally because it was a sort of sacred place connected with Filipa—which I am very sure it is not,' added Marianna reassuringly. 'Tell him all, and that you yourself were definitely not thinking of anyone but him.'

Linda's heart was suddenly very light, and her eyes glowed.

'I will, Marianna! Yes, as soon as I have a chance! If—if you are right, and he should fall in love with me. . . .' She found the rest too difficult to utter, for she could be allowing herself to indulge in wishful thinking, just because of what her sister-in-law had said.

Nevertheless, she left the Casa with hope in her heart, her steps light as she went to the car. Overhead, the sun shone down from a cloudless sky, and in Marianna's garden birds were singing. . . .

The vines had lost their smooth green texture and colour, with the foliage turning golden brown and the grapes standing out, large and luscious, deep purple in colour. Pickers had trouped on to the estate, singing as they came, the younger ones dancing along. It was a time of merrymaking even though there was a good deal of hard work to be done. Rows were cleared systematically, with the pickers singing most of the time. The hillsides were alive with activity. Linda and her aunt helped, this after Linda—not yet having had an opportunity of carrying out her intention of trying to put right her mistake—had asked Duarte if it would be all right if she and her aunt could do some picking. He was in a good mood for the long hot summer had been wonderful for the vines—ever since, in late May and early June, the flower buds had escaped any setbacks so often caused by the weather. Now, the vintage was in full swing and the crop promised to be one of the best for several years.

'If you really want to help then do so by all means,' Duarte had consented, though he did warn that Auntie Sal must not overdo it. 'The sun is still warm and she'll become tired if she stays too long out there, picking.'

Strangely, though, Auntie Sal did not tire all that easily; she was enjoying herself, the new experience, the jovial manner of the pickers, the gaiety of the children who came with them. Marianna's children appeared but Clara was off again in no time at all and her brothers weren't far behind.

'Lazy little blighters,' denounced Auntie Sal, but in a good-humoured voice for all that. She, like her niece, had grown to love the children, each so attractive in his or her own way. 'Clara's a handful, though,' she was often heard to say. 'She needs a man even more than the boys.'

After the picking there came the pressing, no longer done by treading with the feet; all that had gone with the introduction of machinery.

'You seem to have enjoyed yourselves,' was

Duarte's amused comment when at last there was no more work for Linda and her aunt.

'It was great! Duarte, I am going to accept your offer of a home here.'

'I'm glad to hear it,' was his sincere reply, his smile deepening. 'I hope you'll be very happy—and don't forget, all the help you need will be available when you move.'

It was that same night that Linda, having showered and used the body-fragrance which Duarte had once remarked upon, took out a filmy cloud of peach-pearl gossamer nylon from a drawer and put it on. A nightgown fashioned in Paris, sheer and sensuous, it draped her slender body in seductive folds even while its transparency left little to the imagination. She brushed her hair until it shone, used a little perfume on it and tied it back from her face with a ribbon.

The door was firmly closed but she moved resolutely towards it; Duarte was heard for a moment and then there was silence. Had he gone to bed? With the resolve so firm and urgent she knocked rather too loudly and hoped she hadn't vexed him. He opened the door and stood there, taking his fill. She noticed the curling dampness of his hair, not rubbed dry after the shower he had taken. His otherwise naked body was covered with a blue towelling robe with darker blue lapels and cuff trims, and the tie sash was loosely held together with one end threaded over the other—unknotted. The silence stretched; she coloured hotly as it dawned on her that she was here to offer herself, blatantly to ask her husband to make love to her. He of course knew it and that was what was so embarrassing. She heard him say at length,

'You're adorable when you blush like that.' And his hand came out in anticipation of her lowering her face. His flesh was warm beneath her chin; his mastery was exciting as with firmness he made her look into his eyes, and continue to do so for several seconds.

'Duarte . . . I. . . .'

'Yes?' he prompted when she failed to voice what she had come to say to him. 'Yes,' he repeated releasing her chin.

'I want to—to talk,' she stammered. 'You see—'

'To talk?' with a sardonic inflection as his dark eyes roved her figure again. 'I wouldn't have believed you had anything like that in mind,' added her husband with a sort of amused sarcasm which only served to increase her embarrassment.

They were standing in the doorway and she moved backwards, half wishing she had chosen some other time for what she had to say. He followed, so that he was still towering above her, a circumstance which did nothing to help her attempt to regain some modicum of composure.

'I do want to talk,' she managed, staring up at him with a wide and pleading stare. 'Listen, won't you, Duarte? It's important—very.'

For a fleeting moment the eyes became hard and narrowed, the jaw taut, inexorable. But all soon underwent a change and he was showing her that hint of mockery again.

'I had an idea you wanted to say something

about ending the marriage,' he explained. 'But obviously you wouldn't don this kind of attire—'

'Duarte!' she cried, anger rising because he was deliberately making fun of her and because she wanted to get her little speech over and done with. This mood was attractive, she had to own, but for her it did not suit the occasion. 'Will you please listen to what I have to say?'

The dark eyes glittered but again came a change.

'Carry on, then,' he invited and folded his arms as if he expected a long-drawn-out narrative.

Loving him as she did, Linda wondered why she suddenly wanted to hit him!

'That night,' she began, 'when you believed I was thinking of my first husband—I wasn't, Duarte, believe me.'

'Why, then, didn't you say so at the time?' A perfectly reasonable question and one she would have expected.

'It was difficult. . . .' She continued by telling him about her suspicions when they were close to the little arbour. 'And you went there afterwards,' she thought to add and saw the frown of puzzlement that creased his brow.

'I went back afterwards?'

She coloured, and had to admit that this, too, had been nothing more than conjecture.

'You appear to have taken a lot for granted,' was his cold rejoinder. 'You have a vivid imagination, Linda!'

'I'm sorry.' She hung her head; it was jerked almost roughly up again and once more she was compelled to meet his gaze.

'For your information,' he said curtly, 'I wouldn't take you into that particular arbour because, earlier in the day, one of the gardeners came to tell me he had discovered rot in the rustic seat and it wasn't safe to sit on—not that one could fall far, but it didn't seem a good idea to risk any sort of a fall. As for my going back later—' He spread his hands in a gesture of impatience. 'I'm afraid I can't be held responsible for these vivid pictures you create in your mind, Linda. I did not go back to the arbour since it would not have made much sense to do so, would it?' His eyes were dark with censure but there was a glimmer of something else as well, something that set Linda's pulses racing, her heart beating rather too quickly for comfort. She felt breathless and excited, wanted to step up closer to him yet she stepped back instead. Again he followed, this time to take her by the shoulders and make her look at him. Her nerves quivered, affected by emotions rising pleasantly within her. Her tremulous eyes were raised to his cool and unfathomable gaze and for a brief moment he seemed remote, unapproachable. But then his hands tightened as he drew her against him, the very masculine smell of him mingling with body lotion and talc assailing her nostrils, tempting and heady. Her lips parted unconsciously as the silent seconds passed. He slid his eyes to them, gleaming moistly, and more inviting and irresistible than she knew. Duarte's mouth came down to possess them, while his slender brown hands slid round to her back, fingers spreading in downward progress until, masterfully shaping themselves to her soft

170

and fleshy curves, their pressure was increased to bring her so close that his throbbing maleness pushed hard against the soft, resilient flesh of her stomach, communicating its urgent need, and at the same time bringing to vibrant life Linda's own erotic needs and desires. His seeking hands were hot now, searing her skin as they roamed at will to all the vulnerable places, sensitizing her nerve cells, awakening her to full arousal. His mouth was busy, too, moist and mobile, almost cruel in its crushing strength, in its demand that she part her lips in supplication and obedience to his wish. Vibrations shuddered through her entire body as the exploration of his questing tongue brought it circling the inside of her cheek, its roughness an exquisite sensation creating the spread of desire through her loins like a warm flow of air from a tropical sea. She arched against him in primitive abandon and sensuality, her frenzied fingers curling into his thick dark hair.

'You're so desirable. . . .' His throaty whisper was hot against her cheek; his hand came up to thrust within the low neckline of the gossamer and lace creation and capture her breast. The heat of his hand and its strength, the manipulation of its palm on her curve and its fingers on the nipple. . . . All this coalesced to create a burning intensity of longing and all control fled.

'Love me, Duarte,' she whispered throatily. 'Don't tempt me any more. . . .'

But he was not in any hurry, as, holding her from him, he stripped the frail covering from her quivering body and allowed himself the luxury of feasting his eyes on her for long moments of pleasure for him and agony for her. The primordial clamour of wanting him and the fulfilment he could give brought another little pleading moan from her lips. That he revelled in his triumph she did not doubt but with all restraint lost she had no pride to draw away, or to pretend she was as calm as he. It would have been useless anyway for there was nothing that could effectively be hidden from that perceptive gaze. Lifting a hand he loosened the band on her hair and thrust his sensuous fingers deep into the silken mass, tugging slightly as if to remind her yet again that he was her master. She forced herself close just as his gown fell open and again she was made conscious of his virility. Her arms slid upwards, strong about his lean hard shoulders, and then she herself was tempting and teasing, with her hands and her body, curving her pliant frame in rhythmic harmony with his. Triumphantly she gloried in the knowledge that *she* had managed to create full arousal in *him!* His breath was ragged, his hands like vices in their lack of control . . . and instead of a cry of pain to halt him, it was a low little laugh that issued from her lips, a laugh that told of the sheer joy of loving him, and then it was he who was murmuring, in thick and throaty tones quickened by urgency,

'Linda . . . my wife . . . I must have you . . . now!' Sliding his hands right down he curled them to take the weight and she was swung right off her feet and carried to the bed. A snap of the light switch and only moonglow was there to silhouette their figures as he lowered her on to the covers. His robe was thrown aside and he was with her, beside and above her, his knee within her thighs, the vortex of his passion about to be released in a deluge that would carry them both to the gates of heaven . . . and beyond.

# Chapter Ten

It was Christmas Eve and all the family were gathered together at the Palacio. A gay gathering which included a few of Duarte's friends, and the priest, a jovial man who was fun to have in the house. Auntie Sal was there, having moved to the Palacio two months previously. Also present was the Marquez Henrique Guisepe Miguel de Francesco, who had been a regular visitor to the Casa de Rialta for several months.

Much activity had been going on at the Palacio for the past couple of weeks, with Linda being given the task of decorating the giant tree and wrapping the numerous presents. For on the following day there was a party for the workers of the *quinta* and their children when every one of them received a present from the tree. Glittering decorations embellished almost every room on the ground floor, and the entrance hall was a fairyland of colour and light. The fountains in the courtyards were also a spectacle of colour and light.

Following the custom practised in the home of a great *fidalgo*, the main course of the banquet was the typical *pecalhau*—a recipe based on dried salted cod fish which could be 'cooked in a thousand ways' and each one exceedingly tasty. The custom was a survival from ancient times when it was forbidden to eat meat on Christmas Eve.

As the party was not large—all the children having been sent to bed much earlier—the small dining saloon was used. Duarte was at the head of the table and his wife at the other end; on her right was the Marquez and on her left Diaz. On Duarte's right was Auntie Sal, delighted to be so favoured. The priest was the very life of the party, making jokes and quick-witted ripostes all the time, creating laughter that often brought the feasting to a temporary halt. Auntie Sal was several times seen to be wiping her eyes, and it was plain that she was thoroughly enjoying herself.

Linda, eyes tender and a smile on her lips, repeatedly looked at her husband. She had admitted, that night, when in the throes of ecstasy, that she loved him, but it had been another month before he said the words she had feverishly been waiting to hear,

'My wife . . . my Linda, I love you, dearest. I never thought it possible that I could love again, but it only goes to show how little we know of our future.'

175

And since then life had been sheer bliss for them both.

After the dinner was over came the customary ritual of Midnight Mass, after which the priest reluctantly made his departure. He had to be up early in the morning, he said.

'Oh, but I've had the time of my life!' exclaimed Auntie Sal when, most of the others having gone to bed, she had a few minutes alone with her niece. 'Why should I be so lucky?'

'And I,' murmured Linda with a faraway expression on her lovely face. 'Why should I be so lucky, Auntie Sal?' She seemed bewildered all at once and added wonderingly, 'Am I dreaming, love?'

The old lady laughed as she replied,

'It's real, my love, and you deserve everything. I always knew he'd fall in love with you. I said it—'

'Many times,' laughed her niece.

'My prediction was correct.'

'I'm glad you enjoyed the party. Don't forget to put your shoe on the chimneypiece before you go to bed, will you?'

'I almost forgot! What a strange yet charming idea.' She gave a chuckle as she added, 'You can't get much into a shoe, can you—I mean, not much more than a diamond necklace or some such!'

'Now what on earth would you do with a diamond necklace?' Duarte had come softly and was standing behind them, a smile of contentment on his handsome face. How distinguished he looked! thought Linda, with that dinner jacket and the snow white shirt frilled down the front.

'I'd probably give it to Linda,' answered the old lady with another chuckle.

Duarte came round and stood looking down at them both, sitting there on the velvet padded window seat.

'You enjoyed the meal?' He was looking at Auntie Sal who nodded her head vigorously.

'I never thought fish—especially salted, dried fish—could be so delicious.'

'It's the way it's cooked.' He glanced at his watch. 'I think we ought to turn in; we've a very busy day tomorrow.'

As could be expected it was the children who were up first. 'I wanted a huge teddy bear,' said Clara when Linda appeared. 'Where is it?'

'It wouldn't fit in your shoe,' from Felix, laughing.

'Neither would your train set! Where is my teddy!'

'That'll do,' admonished Linda. 'We don't want any tantrums on Christmas morning, do we?'

'It all depends,' retorted her young niece, pouting. 'If I don't get my teddy there'll be more than tantrums!'

'Haven't I always said she wants her bottom smacking.' Auntie Sal had appeared and was frowning at the little girl whose eyes now glistened with tears. Her brothers were not bothering too much, being interested in their own gifts, each having a big bag which had been put on the hearth by their Uncle Duarte.

Inez's children, Miguel and Maria, were also engrossed with what was in their bags, though all the five children had had small presents in their shoes. Now, there was still a long row of shoes on the chimneypiece but Linda and her aunt were waiting for the others to come down before seeing what they had. Both had put a present on the tree for the other; the presents in the shoes were from Duarte only.

Duarte was swooped upon as soon as he came into the room.

'Uncle Duarte, where's my big teddy bear I asked for!'

'You've probably not been given one,' said her mother, entering on her brother's heels. 'If you ask you know very well you don't get.'

But Duarte was frowning as he glanced around.

'There was a teddy bear,' he said, puzzled.

'Then where is it!' Clara stamped her foot and started to cry.

'Don't,' begged Linda taking the child to her and stroking her hair. 'Your teddy must be here somewhere.' For some reason she was becoming tensed, noticing that Maria was not showing the least interest, not like the other children who by now realised something was amiss for their uncle's face was dark and stern. Linda was recalling the fight the two little girls had had yesterday almost as soon as Inez and her family had arrived. Undoubtedly it was Maria's fault; she had marched right up to Clara and viciously tugged her hair, whereupon Clara had instantly retaliated by kicking her cousin on the shins but not content with this she had bitten her arm. Maria was screaming, blaming Clara for it all. Both children were punished by being sent to their rooms by their uncle and ordered to stay there for an hour.

Auntie Sal, who had always said Clara was a wretch, now followed the direction of Linda's gaze and her eyes glinted.

'Do you suppose that vicious little brat has done away with Clara's toy?'

'There's certainly a guilty look about her—'

'Which one of you has had Clara's teddy bear?' Duarte's voice brought instant silence, and attention.

'Not me!' indignantly from Vasco.

'And I haven't seen it either.' Felix spoke mildly. No one would even believe it was he who had had anything to do with the disappearance.

'Miguel?' The stern inflection even made Linda shudder.

'No, Uncle Duarte; it wasn't me.'

Linda and her aunt exchanged glances.

'The little madam!' seethed the old lady. 'Poor little Clara, having a joke like this played on her.'

'She'll have her teddy in a moment,' returned Linda confidently, turning her head as Inez came into the room followed by Diaz and Juan.

'Well, Maria?'

'I haven't done anything!' snapped the girl who was just a year older than Clara. 'Her teddy must be somewhere.' She muttered something in Portuguese, turned her back on the company, and picked up a beautiful doll she had dropped on the floor.

Duarte said softly,

'Which one of you was down first?'

'I wasn't!' swiftly from Maria.

'Is something wrong, Duarte?' Inez came further into the room and cast a glance at her sister. Marianna's mouth was tight.

'Clara's present seems to have disappeared,' Duarte submitted. 'It was in a box.'

Linda hadn't seen any of the presents being put either into the shoes or on the hearth. Duarte had come upstairs with her, kissed her goodnight and said he was off to see to the presents. He wasn't gone long so obviously he had all the presents already wrapped or boxed.

'Who was down first?' inquired Duarte again, still in that dangerously soft tone of voice.

None of the children spoke except Clara who said that when she came down Maria and Vasco were already opening their presents. She had dried her tears but was still leaning against Linda, looking both angry and disappointed.

'I have asked a question.' Duarte's eyes were on Maria's back. 'Turn around,' he ordered but instead she ran to the other side of the room, dragging her doll with her.

'Maria!' Inez's voice was sharp, imperious. 'Were you down first?'

'No, I wasn't! Vasco was down first, so if someone has stolen Clara's teddy it must be him!'

Vasco seemed staggered by the lie.

'You were here when I came into this room, Maria, because I said you must have been up early.'

'What have you done with the teddy?' Duarte

moved and, gripping Maria by the arm in no gentle manner, swung her round to face him. 'Well, I'm waiting.'

'I haven't had the—' She finished the sentence in Portuguese and received an instant and thorough shaking.

'So it's a rotten teddy, is it?' It was Juan who spoke. He had said yesterday to Linda that his sister's two children were definitely not nice and he expressed the hope that they wouldn't cause any trouble while they were here. Apparently they had both played a part, last year, in hiding some of the presents from the tree, with the result that, at the party for the estate workers on Christmas day, there were some presents short. Inez's children had at last owned up and the presents were found outside in one of the stables, their pretty wrappings torn from them.

'What have you done with it?' Inez was as embarrassed as she was angry. She looked at Marianna whose mouth was still compressed.

'This is spoiling everything for Duarte,' whispered Auntie Sal in disgust. 'He'd been expecting us all to be opening our presents by this time.'

He was shaking Maria but to no avail. Clara started to cry again and now it was Marianna who came over to comfort her.

'I w-wanted to—to have a lovely b-big teddy,' she sobbed. 'And I knew Uncle Duarte w-would make sure I got one from—from. . . .' Sobs choked the rest and by now everyone in the room was beginning to feel the effect of this upset.

'Go to your room, Maria, and don't come down

until you are willing to say what you have done with Clara's present.' It was Duarte who spoke, and it did seem that Inez would interfere but her husband, Pedro, standing by her side, shook his head.

'We're guests here, Inez,' he said. 'Duarte has every right to conduct this matter in the way he believes will be most effective.'

Maria started to cry, and within seconds admitted she had thrown the teddy bear into the lake.

'It sank,' she added, escaping from the room by racing to the open door behind her mother.

'In the lake!' screamed Clara. 'Oh, I shall kick her to death!' And she too would have run from the room but Duarte caught her and pulled her back, kicking and screaming and bringing forth a stream of what sounded like dire threats to her cousin's person, but as she was speaking in Portuguese neither Linda nor her aunt could understand a word.

Order was eventually restored, with Duarte promising to get Clara another teddy bear immediately after the holiday was over. But a cloud was hanging over everyone for some time and the opening of the presents was not nearly as happy an occasion as everyone had expected it to be. However, Linda could not let the incident overshadow her pleasure at receiving a diamond and sapphire bracelet from her husband. She kissed him in front of everyone and thanked him—quietly and a little shyly.

The others gathered round to admire it, and also to admire the wristwatch received by Auntie Sal, and the antique brooch which Marianna found in her shoe. Linda had given Duarte book ends in silver gilt, bought from Harrods when she and her aunt had a day's shopping on the occasion when she went to England with Duarte to see Marianna in the hospital.

'I had better go and find Maria,' sighed Inez when they were all ready to go in to breakfast. 'She's quite capable of losing herself deliberately.'

'And cause more trouble,' from Auntie Sal. 'I'd give her the belt if she was my child!'

It was to Clara's credit that not only did she cease making a fuss over the matter of the lost toy, but she was also persuaded not to attack her cousin. She was in fact rather smugly basking in the attention of those adults who sympathised with her and fussed a little. Duarte had no time for this kind of nonsense and neither had Linda, Auntie Sal or Clara's mother. Inez was inclined to fuss a little which, snorted, Auntie Sal, was easily seen as insincere.

'You'll be having a present off the tree,' Duarte reminded Clara, and this, along with the attractive gold bracelet she had had in her shoe, seemed to satisfy her until she could have the teddy bear she had set her heart upon.

Lunch on Christmas Day was a family affair, with only Maria, still in disgrace, not taking part in the general conversation which included the children.

The highlight of the day was of course the big

party, held in the Great Hall, for the estate employees and their children. Linda was glad of her aunt's help for although Duarte employed an army of servants, there seemed to be so much to do that every hand was needed. Sandwiches and cakes, jellies and many other sweets, fruit cake and pies . . . so much to prepare in addition to making sure that every guest had a present from the tree. With last year's near disaster in mind Duarte had ready a number of spare presents, suitable for men, women and children.

There was music and dancing first, then the tea-party with the distribution of presents immediately afterwards. Duarte called out the names, while Linda and her aunt continued to hand him the presents which they had cut from the tree. Auntie Sal was in her element and so was Linda. She was particularly happy, knowing of the two special announcements which her husband was to make at the end of the party.

Dancers came in to perform, and guitar music accompanied them. Portuguese songs were then sung, some sad, some gay. And at last it was time for the party to break up. Duarte always gave a speech, in which among other things he thanked his employees one and all for their loyalty and attention to duty. This year all was rather different for now he had a wife standing beside him, a wife who already had become popular with many working on the *quinta*. She was interested in their customs, had begun learning Portuguese, and now. . . .

Duarte having given his speech and been cheered, held up his hand for silence.

'I have two announcements to make which I know will interest you all and, I think, give you as much pleasure to hear as they give me to announce. The first is that Dona Marianna my sister is soon to marry the Marquez Henrique Guisepe Miguel de Francesco—' Cheers broke out even before he had finished. Marianna was with her fiancé, their fingers entwined. There were calls for the Marquez who came reluctantly to the dais on which Duarte was standing. He was rather shy but Linda had from the first found him charming and had wondered how Marianna could have given him up. Marianna admitted that she now did not know herself, but at the time she was young and wilful, resenting the arranged marriage, and so she had asserted her independence and gone away with the man who was later to desert her. The divorce was going through swiftly, being undefended, and the couple were expected to be married in the late spring or early summer. Auntie Sal would then be moving to the Casa, and there had been talk that Alice might come over and share it, since its layout was such that it could easily make two separate apartments.

When the Marquez had finished there were more cheers, and then a hush fell as once again Duarte called for silence.

'My second announcement is . . .' His voice tailed off fleetingly as he caught his wife's flushed face in his vision.

'He shouldn't,' said her aunt, who had mounted the dais to stand beside her.

'It's customary, Auntie—'

'My next announcement is that my wife and I are expecting an increase in our family in June.'

The applause this time was deafening, for the employees had waited a long time for an announcement like this. Cheers rang to the roof, prolonged cheers that seemed never to end even though Duarte was holding up his hand.

They died down eventually though, and a fado was sung for the prospective parents. Someone had evidently had it ready, just in case!

At last Linda and her husband were alone in her bedroom. She had sunk down on the bed, almost exhausted, but Duarte could not resist bringing her to her feet and kissing her long and hard on the mouth.

'My love,' he whispered close to her cheek. 'They all adore you.'

'I'm so happy, Duarte. Who would have thought, when we decided to marry, that we'd come to love each other like this?'

'The human heart doesn't like to be starved,' he returned seriously. 'I guess we were both destined to fall in love again and so here we are, together for always, and with our baby on the way.' He held her at arm's length so he could look deeply into her eyes. 'You've changed my life, darling, given me the fulfilment it had lacked for so long.' His eyes were dark with tender emotion and she clung to him, unable for the moment to speak, so filled with emotion were her own heart and mind. But eventually she was able to say, her soft lips murmuring against his own,

'And you've changed my life, dearest. I'm living again, and we've so much to do together and to look forward to. . . .' Again emotion prevented speech and she just arched close and rested her head on his breast. And for a long while they stayed like that, content in their silence and nearness and with the sure knowledge that they had found something so precious that no trials and tribulations could ever rob them of it. Fate had brought them together in a way neither had ever expected. And now a deep and abiding love was theirs.

After a long while Duarte bent his head and took her lips, meaning to be gentle, to leave her to rest and go to his own room, but her arms and lips and body sent out the silent message he really wanted to receive, and with rising ardour and desire he swept her into the vortex of primitive passion she had come to know so well.

'You're sure you're not tired, darling,' he felt he had to ask despite her eager reciprocation. She gave a low laugh, tucked a warm hand into his shirt and said coquettishly,

'Try leaving me, darling,' and he laughed then and, pulling off the négligé she had put on before he came up and joined her, he swept her into his arms and strode purposefully across the room.

It was a long time later that, gathered safely into

his arms, and with her legs entwined in his, she whispered her good night.

'Good night, my dearest love,' he whispered back, his cool clean breath fanning her cheek. 'Sleep peacefully . . . and thank you, darling, for coming to me.'

## IT'S YOUR OWN SPECIAL TIME
*Contemporary romances for today's women.
Each month, six very special love stories will be yours
from SILHOUETTE. Look for them wherever books are sold
or order now from the coupon below.*

## $1.50 each

| | | | |
|---|---|---|---|
| ☐ 5 Goforth | ☐ 28 Hampson | ☐ 54 Beckman | ☐ 83 Halston |
| ☐ 6 Stanford | ☐ 29 Wildman | ☐ 55 LaDame | ☐ 84 Vitek |
| ☐ 7 Lewis | ☐ 30 Dixon | ☐ 56 Trent | ☐ 85 John |
| ☐ 8 Beckman | ☐ 32 Michaels | ☐ 57 John | ☐ 86 Adams |
| ☐ 9 Wilson | ☐ 33 Vitek | ☐ 58 Stanford | ☐ 87 Michaels |
| ☐ 10 Caine | ☐ 34 John | ☐ 59 Vernon | ☐ 88 Stanford |
| ☐ 11 Vernon | ☐ 35 Stanford | ☐ 60 Hill | ☐ 89 James |
| ☐ 17 John | ☐ 38 Browning | ☐ 61 Michaels | ☐ 90 Major |
| ☐ 19 Thornton | ☐ 39 Sinclair | ☐ 62 Halston | ☐ 92 McKay |
| ☐ 20 Fulford | ☐ 46 Stanford | ☐ 63 Brent | ☐ 93 Browning |
| ☐ 22 Stephens | ☐ 47 Vitek | ☐ 71 Ripy | ☐ 94 Hampson |
| ☐ 23 Edwards | ☐ 48 Wildman | ☐ 73 Browning | ☐ 95 Wisdom |
| ☐ 24 Healy | ☐ 49 Wisdom | ☐ 76 Hardy | ☐ 96 Beckman |
| ☐ 25 Stanford | ☐ 50 Scott | ☐ 78 Oliver | ☐ 97 Clay |
| ☐ 26 Hastings | ☐ 52 Hampson | ☐ 81 Roberts | ☐ 98 St. George |
| ☐ 27 Hampson | ☐ 53 Browning | ☐ 82 Dailey | ☐ 99 Camp |

## $1.75 each

| | | | |
|---|---|---|---|
| ☐ 100 Stanford | ☐ 110 Trent | ☐ 120 Carroll | ☐ 130 Hardy |
| ☐ 101 Hardy | ☐ 111 South | ☐ 121 Langan | ☐ 131 Stanford |
| ☐ 102 Hastings | ☐ 112 Stanford | ☐ 122 Scofield | ☐ 132 Wisdom |
| ☐ 103 Cork | ☐ 113 Browning | ☐ 123 Sinclair | ☐ 133 Rowe |
| ☐ 104 Vitek | ☐ 114 Michaels | ☐ 124 Beckman | ☐ 134 Charles |
| ☐ 105 Eden | ☐ 115 John | ☐ 125 Bright | ☐ 135 Logan |
| ☐ 106 Dailey | ☐ 116 Lindley | ☐ 126 St. George | ☐ 136 Hampson |
| ☐ 107 Bright | ☐ 117 Scott | ☐ 127 Roberts | ☐ 137 Hunter |
| ☐ 108 Hampson | ☐ 118 Dailey | ☐ 128 Hampson | ☐ 138 Wilson |
| ☐ 109 Vernon | ☐ 119 Hampson | ☐ 129 Converse | ☐ 139 Vitek |

## $1.75 each

| | | | |
|---|---|---|---|
| ☐ 140 Erskine | ☐ 161 Trent | ☐ 181 Terrill | ☐ 201 Starr |
| ☐ 142 Browning | ☐ 162 Ashby | ☐ 182 Clay | ☐ 202 Hampson |
| ☐ 143 Roberts | ☐ 163 Roberts | ☐ 183 Stanley | ☐ 203 Browning |
| ☐ 144 Goforth | ☐ 164 Browning | ☐ 184 Hardy | ☐ 204 Carroll |
| ☐ 145 Hope | ☐ 165 Young | ☐ 185 Hampson | ☐ 205 Maxam |
| ☐ 146 Michaels | ☐ 166 Wisdom | ☐ 186 Howard | ☐ 206 Manning |
| ☐ 147 Hampson | ☐ 167 Hunter | ☐ 187 Scott | ☐ 207 Windham |
| ☐ 148 Cork | ☐ 168 Carr | ☐ 188 Cork | ☐ 208 Halston |
| ☐ 149 Saunders | ☐ 169 Scott | ☐ 189 Stephens | ☐ 209 LaDame |
| ☐ 150 Major | ☐ 170 Ripy | ☐ 190 Hampson | ☐ 210 Eden |
| ☐ 151 Hampson | ☐ 171 Hill | ☐ 191 Browning | ☐ 211 Walters |
| ☐ 152 Halston | ☐ 172 Browning | ☐ 192 John | ☐ 212 Young |
| ☐ 153 Dailey | ☐ 173 Camp | ☐ 193 Trent | ☐ 213 Dailey |
| ☐ 154 Beckman | ☐ 174 Sinclair | ☐ 194 Barry | ☐ 214 Hampson |
| ☐ 155 Hampson | ☐ 175 Jarrett | ☐ 195 Dailey | ☐ 215 Roberts |
| ☐ 156 Sawyer | ☐ 176 Vitek | ☐ 196 Hampson | ☐ 216 Saunders |
| ☐ 157 Vitek | ☐ 177 Dailey | ☐ 197 Summers | ☐ 217 Vitek |
| ☐ 158 Reynolds | ☐ 178 Hampson | ☐ 198 Hunter | ☐ 218 Hunter |
| ☐ 159 Tracy | ☐ 179 Beckman | ☐ 199 Roberts | ☐ 219 Cork |
| ☐ 160 Hampson | ☐ 180 Roberts | ☐ 200 Lloyd | |

## $1.95 each

_#220 THE DAWN IS GOLDEN, Hampson

_#221 PRACTICAL DREAMER, Browning

_#222 TWO FACES OF LOVE, Carroll

_#223 A PRIVATE EDEN, Summers

_#224 HIDDEN ISLE, Langan

_#225 DELTA RIVER MAGIC, St. George

_#226 SWEET SECOND LOVE, Hampson

_#227 FORBIDDEN AFFAIR, Beckman

_#228 DANCE AT YOUR WEDDING, King

_#229 FOR ERIC'S SAKE, Thornton

_#230 IVORY INNOCENCE, Stevens

_#231 WESTERN MAN, Dailey

---

## SILHOUETTE BOOKS, Department SB/1

1230 Avenue of the Americas
New York, NY 10020

Please send me the books I have checked above. I am enclosing $_____
(please add 50¢ to cover postage and handling. NYS and NYC residents please
add appropriate sales tax). Send check or money order—no cash or C.O.D.'s
please. Allow six weeks for delivery.

NAME _____

ADDRESS _____

CITY _____ STATE/ZIP _____

# Genuine Silhouette
# sterling silver bookmark
# for only $15.95!

What a beautiful way to hold your place in your current romance! This genuine sterling silver bookmark, with the distinctive Silhouette symbol in elegant black, measures 1½″ long and 1″ wide. It makes a beautiful gift for yourself, and for every romantic you know! And, at only $15.95 each, including all postage and handling charges, you'll want to order several now, while supplies last.